5-7-02
B

D1266975

Hamilton's Principle and
Physical Systems

ACADEMIC PAPERBACKS*

EDITED BY Henry Booker, D. Allan Bromley, Nicholas DeClaris, W. Magnus, Alvin Nason, and A. Shenitzer

*Most of these volumes are also available in a cloth bound edition.

Hamilton's Principle and Physical Systems

B. R. GOSSICK
UNIVERSITY OF KENTUCKY
LEXINGTON, KENTUCKY

1967

ACADEMIC PRESS *New York and London*

ACADEMIC PRESS INC.
111 Fifth Avenue, New York, New York 10003

United Kingdom Edition published by
ACADEMIC PRESS INC. (LONDON) LTD.
Berkeley Square House, London W.1

LIBRARY OF CONGRESS CATALOG CARD NUMBER: 66-30083

PRINTED IN THE UNITED STATES OF AMERICA

To my wife, Jean

Preface

For a number of years the different scientific disciplines have been overlapping more and more, and demands for a greater breadth of performance in the professions of engineering, physics, and chemistry have been felt. Thus, to meet this demand there has been a trend toward a more catholic pedagogy, bringing about an increased emphasis on the generality and symmetry of the theories in these different disciplines. In keeping with that trend, the aim of this text is to provide a comprehensive treatment of mechanical and electromagnetic systems, at a level suitable for senior undergraduate and beginning graduate students.

Hamilton's principle is used herein as the basis for treating each generic type of physical system. Because of the scope of this treatment, and in order to have a concise text, it has been necessary to select certain examples of interest without any attempt at completeness. In selecting examples to illustrate basic principles, an effort has been made to expose the student to useful practical applications. Such traditional examples as a bead constrained to move on a frictionless rod, and Atwood's machine have not been used, whereas problems in electrical circuits and electronic systems have been used.

The first three chapters are introductory, Chapter 1 being a historical synopsis on analytical mechanics, Chapter 2 a mathematical compendium, and Chapter 3 a presentation of Hamilton's action integral. Conservative systems are treated in Chapter 4 where it is indicated how Hamilton's principle may be applied to mechanical systems with coordinates representing either rectilinear or angular displacement, and to electromagnetic systems with coordinates representing charges. Chapter 5 is devoted to nonconservative linear systems. A Lagrangian formulation for nonconservative linear systems is presented and it is shown that this formulation satisfies Hamilton's principle. The Lagrangian density is treated in Chapter 6. Several methods of taking into account such features of a physical system as its uniformity, isotropy, or periodicity are presented. In closing, a few generalizations relating analytical mechanics to modern physics are mentioned.

As the application of Hamilton's principle to nonconservative linear systems covers a wide range of systems, and, as far as the author is aware, has not appeared previously in other texts, it seems to deserve special mention. This method has two advantages over the standard treatment of nonconservative systems after Lord Rayleigh: (1) it applies to a wider class of problems (radiation damping is included), and (2) it includes a demonstration that the Lagrangian formulation satisfies Hamilton's principle, which brings a larger body of systems under one postulate.

It is well known that the theories of physics may be arranged in different schemes, with certain postulates in one system appearing as theorems in another, and vice versa. Given two schemes for the same domain of physics, each having the same number of postulates, one still might take precedence over the other, i.e., if that particular scheme could be shown to apply also to another domain of physics. It follows that if mechanical systems and electromagnetic systems are treated together in one consistent scheme, then definitely something has been gained. The following remarks illustrate how the two systems are brought together. Newton's second law is a postulate in elementary mechanics, and in elementary electromagnetic circuit theory Kirchhoff's law of voltage summation is a postulate. However, in the scheme presented here, both Newton's second law and Kirchhoff's law of voltage summation are merely different examples that follow directly from Theorem I. In the last chapter some of the field equations of classical electromagnetic theory are obtained as the limits of difference equations based on the Lagrangian density.

In summary, a comprehensive elementary presentation of classical mechanics and electricity and magnetism is given here. Parenthetically it should be added that the main arguments used herein are prominent in the history of electromagnetic theory.

It is a pleasure to acknowledge the helpful comments of Mr. H. Seidel, Professor George E. Moore, and of the editors, Professor Henry Booker and Professor Nicholas DeClaris.

September, 1967   B. R. GOSSICK

Contents

Contents

Note to the Reader

There has been a tendency for engineers and physicists to develop graphosclerosis (rigidity of notation) along arbitrarily different lines. As this is an attempt at an interdisciplinary text, it is well to point out some of the common conventions, and also those we have elected to use in this book. Electrical engineers commonly designate $\sqrt{-1}$ as j whereas mathematicians and physicists generally use i. The latter has been used here. Take a plane wave with a plane of constant phase $\theta = \mathbf{r} \cdot \mathbf{k}$. Engineers express the amplitude of such a wave in the Euler form,

$$\psi(\mathbf{r}, t) = \psi_0 \exp i \left[\omega t - \theta(\mathbf{r}) \right]$$

while physicists write it as follows:

$$\psi(\mathbf{r}, t) = \psi_0 \exp i \left[\theta(\mathbf{r}) - \omega t \right].$$

Thus, on a D'Argand diagram ωt progresses counterclockwise with time t for engineers, and clockwise for physicists; in this book the custom of the engineers has been followed frequently but not exclusively. Furthermore, we might have defined the *complex power* either as

$$\mathscr{P}^* = \frac{1}{t_2 - t_1} \int_{t_1}^{t_2} \frac{\mathbf{J}^* \cdot \dot{\mathbf{r}}}{2} \, dt,$$

or

$$\mathscr{P}^* = \frac{1}{t_2 - t_1} \int_{t_1}^{t_2} \frac{\dot{\mathbf{r}}^* \cdot \mathbf{J}}{2} \, dt,$$

with $\mathbf{J}$ an external force. The choice is arbitrary, and we took the former. Therefore, those readers who feel we have the signs reversed on the imaginary terms of the *complex power* can adjust matters to their own satisfaction by using the alternative definition of the *complex power*.

CHAPTER 1

A Brief
Historical Introduction

Although classical mechanics may be formulated in several ways, there is one that has a universal appeal, which establishes classical mechanics as a class of isoperimetrical problems.[†] It is this formulation, often referred to as analytical mechanics, that constitutes the subject of this text.

Dido, the founder and first queen of Carthage, is celebrated for having been the first to recognize and appreciate the significance of an isoperimetrical problem. She negotiated a real estate transaction with a chieftain of North Africa, in which the amount of land was specified as that which could be enclosed with a certain ox hide. Then Dido cut that hide into the thinnest possible strips and tied them together to form the boundary of a very large territory. This historic transaction is still commemorated in the literature of mathematics and analytical mechanics.

The Alexandrian, Hero, is another ancient credited with having treated an isoperimetrical problem. He proved the theorem that when light passes from one point to another and its path is broken by mirrors, it follows a total path length which is a minimum. This problem was extended by the seventeenth century mathematician, Fermat, who considered light propagating through media of varying index, and discovered that light passes from one place to another in minimum time.

Isoperimetrical problems in mechanics had remained unrecognized up to 1696, when Gottfried Leibnitz and Johann Bernoulli proposed the famous problem of the brachistochrone. The problem is to determine the shape of the curve down which

[†] Isoperimetrical problems, $\iota\sigma\circ\varsigma$ (equal) + $\pi\epsilon\rho\iota\mu\epsilon\tau\rho\circ\nu$ (circumference), are problems in which is sought a curve of fixed length that possesses some maximum property.

a frictionless mass must slide under a constant gravitational force so as to pass from the upper point to the lower in the least time. This was transmitted to the mathematicians of Europe as a challenge, and when Sir Isaac Newton heard about it he solved it immediately. Somewhat later Leonhard Euler (1707–1783) put several problems of mechanics into isoperimetrical form at the suggestion of Daniel Bernoulli (1700–1782). Finally, W. R. Hamilton (1805–1865) obtained the general isoperimetrical formulation of mechanics. The equations of motion which came from Hamilton's isoperimetrical statement of mechanics had been obtained earlier by Joseph Lagrange (1736–1813) from other considerations, and as a consequence, this treatment of mechanics sometimes goes under the name of Lagrangian mechanics.

The interest in analytical mechanics during the eighteenth century and the first half of the nineteenth century was concentrated largely on celestial mechanics, and on a philosophical concern for finding an underlying principle. It was the latter which engaged the attention of Pierre Maupertuis (1698–1759) who felt that the isoperimetrical nature of mechanics constituted a proof for the existence of God. As the laws of nature provide descriptions of, rather than explanations for, physical events, there was an understandable temptation to regard the isoperimetrical law of mechanics as something distinctly different from other laws, i.e., as an edict from the Almighty directing that events take place with an economy of effort.

Meanwhile the generality of mechanics was being tested in areas which were at that time less understood, e.g., the propagation of light, and the behavior of electricity and magnetism, the interrelations between which were only suspected. Thomas Young (1773–1829) and Augustin Fresnel (1788–1827) treated the propagation of light in a medium in terms of transverse vibrations in an elastic solid. Lord Kelvin (1824–1907) and J. C. Maxwell (1831–1879) employed mechanical models to obtain solutions for problems in electrodynamics and the entire development of the classical theory of electricity and magnetism drew heavily upon the generality of analytical mechanics. Thus we have been left with such terms as *elastance, aether, flux, potential,* and *displacement.* We need only look at the formula for differential work

$$dW = \mathbf{J} \; (force) \cdot d\mathbf{r} \; (displacement) \qquad (100.1)$$

and compare it with the formula for the differential energy density of an electric field

$$du = \mathbf{E} \; (force) \cdot d\mathbf{D} \; (displacement) \qquad (100.2)$$

to see how the term, *displacement vector,* originated.[†] Now that we have a satisfactory classical theory of electricity and magnetism, we need not discard the mechanical origins of its theoretical framework. To allow them to remain strengthens the foundation by illustrating that classical electromagnetic theory may be harmoniously included in analytical mechanics.

Before taking up the details of how masses, charges, electric and magnetic fields may be treated by Lagrangian mechanics, attention will be given to some common mathematical methods.

[†] The following quotations are taken from "Electromagnetic Theory," by Oliver Heaviside, Vol. I, Chapter II, Sections 20, 21 (reprinted by Dover, New York, 1950). "If $\mathbf{E}$ be the electric force at any point and $\mathbf{D}$ the displacement, we have $\mathbf{D} = c\mathbf{E}$ .... When the fluxes vary, their rates of increase $\dot{\mathbf{D}}$ and $\dot{\mathbf{B}}$ are the velocities corresponding to the forces $\mathbf{E}$ and $\mathbf{H}$, ... The work spent in producing the fluxes ... is, therefore,

$$U = \int_0^{\mathbf{D}} \mathbf{E} \cdot d\mathbf{D}, \qquad T = \int_0^{\mathbf{B}} \mathbf{H} \cdot d\mathbf{B}."$$

Mathematical Compendium

One is confronted with somewhat of a dilemma in deciding what mathematical background to assume in a text with inter-disciplinary objectives. As that background varies from one field to another, it is inevitable that a mathematical compendium which is useful to some readers will be unnecessary to others. Be that as it may, some familiarity with determinants, matrices, and differential equations has been assumed throughout the text. This chapter contains a brief review of some of the common mathematical methods that are used in the later chapters.

2.0.0. Quadratic Forms

Consider the following quadratic expression

$$\begin{aligned} F(x_1, x_2, x_3) = {} & a_{11}x_1^2 + a_{12}x_1x_2 + a_{13}x_1x_3 \\ & + a_{21}x_2x_1 + a_{22}x_2^2 + a_{23}x_2x_3 + a_{31}x_3x_1 \\ & + a_{32}x_3x_2 + a_{33}x_3^2, \end{aligned} \tag{200.1}$$

in which the coefficients of the cross product terms are unequal, e.g., $a_{12} \neq a_{21}$, $a_{13} \neq a_{31}$, and $a_{23} \neq a_{32}$. Let us now designate the arithmetic mean of those coefficients by the following relations

$$\alpha_{12} = \alpha_{21} = \tfrac{1}{2}(a_{12} + a_{21}), \qquad \alpha_{13} = \alpha_{31} = \tfrac{1}{2}(a_{13} + a_{31}),$$
$$\alpha_{23} = \alpha_{32} = \tfrac{1}{2}(a_{23} + a_{32}), \tag{200.2}$$

and use those relations to rewrite (200.1) in the concise form

$$\begin{aligned} F(x_1, x_2, x_3) = {} & \alpha_{11}x_1^2 + 2\alpha_{12}x_1x_2 + 2\alpha_{13}x_1x_3 \\ & + \alpha_{22}x_2^2 + 2\alpha_{23}x_2x_3 + \alpha_{33}x_3^2. \end{aligned} \tag{200.3}$$

The quadratic form (200.3) may be written simply as $x_i{}^*\alpha_{ij}x_j$ in which the sum is taken over repeated indices according to the well known *summation convention*. With the elements of the matrix x_i, real, as is assumed here, its transpose is written x_i^*. In some cases within the text the elements of a matrix x_i are complex and the conjugate transpose of such a matrix is written x_i^*. The quadratic form (200.3) is rewritten below in matrix notation

$$F(x_1, x_2, x_3) = x_i^* \alpha_{ij} x_j$$
$$= (x_1 \quad x_2 \quad x_3) \begin{pmatrix} \alpha_{11} & \alpha_{12} & \alpha_{13} \\ \alpha_{12} & \alpha_{22} & \alpha_{23} \\ \alpha_{13} & \alpha_{23} & \alpha_{33} \end{pmatrix} \begin{pmatrix} x_1 \\ x_2 \\ x_3 \end{pmatrix}. \qquad (200.4)$$

A substitution of the kind illustrated by (200.2) may be always made on any quadratic form, as on (200.1), to permit writing the quadratic form with a square *symmetric* matrix α_{ij} as in (200.4).

Let us now make a linear transformation of the coordinates x_i converting them to a new set of coordinates z_j, as indicated by the following expression

$$x_i = b_{ij} z_j. \qquad (200.5)$$

Replacing each coordinate x_i in the quadratic form (200.4) by its value given in (200.5) gives the following expression which is equivalent to (200.4),

$$F(x_1, x_2, x_3)$$
$$= (z_1 \quad z_2 \quad z_3) \begin{pmatrix} b_{11} & b_{21} & b_{31} \\ b_{12} & b_{22} & b_{32} \\ b_{13} & b_{23} & b_{33} \end{pmatrix} \begin{pmatrix} \alpha_{11} & \alpha_{12} & \alpha_{13} \\ \alpha_{12} & \alpha_{22} & \alpha_{23} \\ \alpha_{13} & \alpha_{23} & \alpha_{33} \end{pmatrix}$$
$$\begin{pmatrix} b_{11} & b_{12} & b_{13} \\ b_{21} & b_{22} & b_{23} \\ b_{31} & b_{32} & b_{33} \end{pmatrix} \begin{pmatrix} z_1 \\ z_2 \\ z_3 \end{pmatrix} = F(z_1, z_2, z_3), \qquad (200.6)$$

which may also be written in more concise notation as

$$F(z_1, z_2, z_3) = z_i^* b_{ij}^* \alpha_{jk} b_{km} z_m. \qquad (200.7)$$

But, it is possible, of course, to write the quadratic form (200.7) in a way that would correspond to (200.4), e.g.,

$$F(z_1, z_2, z_3) = z_i^* \beta_{im} z_m. \tag{200.8}$$

Therefore, by (200.7) and (200.8) we have a square matrix

$$\beta_{im} = b_{ij}^* \alpha_{jk} b_{km},$$

or

$$\begin{pmatrix} \beta_{11} & \beta_{12} & \beta_{13} \\ \beta_{12} & \beta_{22} & \beta_{23} \\ \beta_{13} & \beta_{23} & \beta_{33} \end{pmatrix} = \begin{pmatrix} b_{11} & b_{21} & b_{31} \\ b_{12} & b_{22} & b_{32} \\ b_{13} & b_{23} & b_{33} \end{pmatrix}$$
$$\cdot \begin{pmatrix} \alpha_{11} & \alpha_{12} & \alpha_{13} \\ \alpha_{12} & \alpha_{22} & \alpha_{23} \\ \alpha_{13} & \alpha_{23} & \alpha_{33} \end{pmatrix} \begin{pmatrix} b_{11} & b_{12} & b_{13} \\ b_{21} & b_{22} & b_{23} \\ b_{31} & b_{32} & b_{33} \end{pmatrix}. \tag{200.9}$$

The relationship between the square matrices α_{ij} and β_{ij} is referred to as *congruence*, and α_{ij} is said to be congruent to β_{ij}. The process of obtaining (200.6) by substituting (200.5) into (200.4), demonstrates that a quadratic form is inherently invariant under a linear transformation of coordinates.

Now take a special case of a transformation of coordinates, viz., a rotation of orthogonal coordinates. Consider two Cartesian systems whose origins coincide, one system with coordinates x_i being obtained from the other with coordinates x_j' through a rotation by the following linear transformation:

$$x_i = c_{ij} x_j'. \tag{200.10}$$

The distance from the common origin is the same, as measured in either system, and its square is a simple example of the invariance of the quadratic form, e.g.,

$$x_j^{*'} x_j' = x_i^* x_i. \tag{200.11}$$

By substituting (200.10) into (200.11), we have

$$x_j^{*'} x_j' = (c_{ij} x_j')^* (c_{ij} x_j'), \tag{200.12}$$

which may be rearranged to read

$$x_j^{*\prime} x_j^{\prime} = x_i^{*\prime} c_{ij}^* c_{jk} x_k^{\prime} . \qquad (200.13)$$

By comparing (200.11) with (200.13), we may notice the important property of the rotation matrix c_{ij}, given by the following relation

$$c_{ij}^* c_{jk} = \delta_{ik} , \qquad (200.14)$$

in which δ_{ik} denotes the *Kronecker delta*.

2.0.1. Vectors and Pseudovectors

The elements of either a column or row matrix often represent the coordinates which define the configuration of a particular physical system. Accordingly, the time derivatives of those elements form another column or row matrix which gives the velocity configuration of that system. Sometimes these coordinates represent points in a Cartesian space, but they may also represent angles, or even the electric charges on different parts of the system; in general the coordinates of the system represented by a column or row matrix are those variables that enter into the physical properties of the system. Ordinarily, the coordinates are represented as a column matrix. When a quadratic form is required, then both the column matrix and its transpose are used in the same expression (200.4).

Among the common transformations made on the coordinates of a physical system are the rotation (200.10) and the inversion, i.e.,

$$x_i = -\delta_{ij} x_j^{\prime} . \qquad (201.1)$$

When the spatial coordinates of a physical system are transformed by either (200.10) or (210.1), the vectors of that system may undergo a change in sign, but the pseudovectors (or axial vectors) may undergo a change in sign only for the transformation (200.10). Several examples of vectors and pseudovectors now follow.

Consider the Cartesian coordinates (x_1, x_2, x_3) of a point mass. The location of the mass, given by the radius vector

$$\mathbf{r} = \begin{pmatrix} x_1 \\ x_2 \\ x_3 \end{pmatrix}, \tag{201.2}$$

the velocity

$$\dot{\mathbf{r}} = \begin{pmatrix} \dot{x}_1 \\ \dot{x}_2 \\ \dot{x}_3 \end{pmatrix}, \tag{201.3}$$

and an external force $\mathbf{J}$ exerted on the mass

$$\mathbf{J} = \begin{pmatrix} J_1 \\ J_2 \\ J_3 \end{pmatrix}, \tag{201.4}$$

are all vectors. Now consider that mass to be moving in a circular orbit as indicated in Fig. 2.1. Although the radius vector $\mathbf{r}$ varies its direction with time so as to describe a circle, it remains constant in magnitude. By referring to the diagram (Fig. 2.1), it may be seen that the variation in the radius vector may be written as the following cross product

$$d\mathbf{r} = d\boldsymbol{\theta} \times \mathbf{r}, \tag{201.5}$$

and therefore, we have for the velocity

$$\dot{\mathbf{r}} = \dot{\boldsymbol{\theta}} \times \mathbf{r}. \tag{201.6}$$

As $\mathbf{r}$ in both (201.5) and (201.6), and $d\mathbf{r}$ in (201.5) and $\dot{\mathbf{r}}$ in (201.6) must all change sign if the coordinates are transformed by (201.1), then it is necessary that the transformation leave $d\boldsymbol{\theta}$ in (201.5) and $\dot{\boldsymbol{\theta}}$ in (201.6) unchanged in sign. Hence, $d\boldsymbol{\theta}$ and $\dot{\boldsymbol{\theta}}$ are pseudovectors. The angular momentum of the point mass under discussion may be written

$$\mathbf{f} = m\mathbf{r} \times \dot{\mathbf{r}}.\qquad(201.7)$$

As $\mathbf{r}$ and $\dot{\mathbf{r}}$ enter into (201.7) as a product, the transformation of coordinates (201.1) leaves the angular momentum $\mathbf{f}$ unchanged in sign. Therefore, the angular momentum $\mathbf{f}$ is a pseudovector.

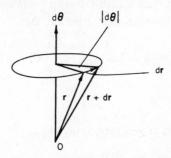

Fig. 2.1.   Illustration of the variation of a radius vector.

2.1.0. Fourier Series and the Generalized Fourier Integral

Subject to certain restrictions given later, a periodic real function $V(t) = V(t \pm n_1 T)$ with T the period, and $n_1 = 1, 2, 3, 4, 5...$, may be expressed by either of the following *Fourier series*:

$$V(t) = \sum_k C_k e^{ik\omega t}, \quad k = 0, \pm 1, \pm 2, \pm 3, ..., \pm \infty,\qquad(210.1)$$

$$V(t) = 2 \sum_{k=0}^{\infty} |C_k| \sin(k\omega t + \theta_k),\qquad(210.2)$$

with

$$\omega = 2\pi/T,\qquad(210.3)$$

$$C_{-k} = C_k^*,\qquad(210.4)$$

and

$$\tan \theta_k = i(C_k^* + C_k)/(C_k^* - C_k).\qquad(210.5)$$

It may be seen by (210.2) that the magnitude $2|C_k|$ is an amplitude associated with the frequency $k\omega$. Coefficients of the kind C_k will be referred to in the text as spectral amplitudes. Comparing two different periodic functions, which have equal periods, the distinction between the two may be made from the fact that each is characterized by a different set of spectral amplitudes C_k. As is well known, the spectral amplitude C_k is determined by multiplying both sides of (210.1) by $\exp[-ik'\omega t]$ and integrating with respect to the time over a period, e.g.,

$$\int_{-T/2}^{T/2} V(t) \exp[-ik'\omega t]\, dt = \sum_{-\infty}^{\infty} \int_{-T/2}^{T/2} C_k \exp[i(k-k')\omega t]\, dt \tag{210.6}$$

$$= TC_{k'}. \tag{210.7}$$

By inserting (210.3) into (210.7) we obtain

$$C_{k'} = \frac{\omega}{2\pi} \int_{-\pi/\omega}^{\pi/\omega} V(t) \exp[-ik'\omega t]\, dt. \tag{210.8}$$

It is clear from (210.6) that a necessary condition on $V(t)$ is the convergence of the integral $\int_{-T/2}^{T/2} |V(t)|\, dt$. Furthermore, the function must be periodic, single-valued and sectionally continuous, i.e., continuous throughout the period with the possible exception of a finite number of finite discontinuities or maxima and minima.

It is obvious that periodic functions encompass a broad domain in the mathematical description of physical events. There is nothing to preclude making the fundamental period extend over the time interval under investigation, so that all pertinent information is conveyed by the function during one period. The following special case of the Fourier series provides an intermediate step between the Fourier series and the Fourier integral, and it also serves to introduce the Born-Kármán boundary conditions.

Let t_1 be the minimum interval which can be resolved, and let $2\pi/t_1$ be the maximum frequency that can be observed. Then let the duration of the fundamental period be given by $T = Nt_1$ with N a very large even integer. We take a periodic function as before:

$$F(t) = F(t \pm n_1 T), \qquad n_1 = 1, 2, 3, ... \qquad (210.9)$$

The boundary conditions applied to a general solution $F(t)$, by making that solution periodic in the manner indicated by (210.9), are called the Born-Kármán conditions. As the product of the fundamental period and the fundamental frequency must equal 2π, we have the following relation

$$\omega = \frac{2\pi}{T} = \frac{2\pi}{Nt_1}. \qquad (210.10)$$

We write the periodic function using a relation of the kind given by (210.1), except that we take a finite sum whose limits are established by the maximum interval over which the frequency can be observed:

$$F(t) = \sum_{-N/2}^{N/2} C_k e^{ik\omega t}. \qquad (210.11)$$

Equation (210.11) may be applied to a wide variety of physical problems, by making N suitably large and t_1 suitably small.

The following function may be used to represent an impulse,

$$I(t) = N/n, \qquad 0 < t < nt_1$$
$$= 0, \qquad \text{otherwise throughout the period } 0 < t < T,$$

and

$$= I(t \pm n_1 T), \qquad (210.12)$$

and it may be expressed by (210.11) with the spectral amplitudes given by the following relation

$$C_k = \left(\frac{\sin \frac{1}{2} k\omega n t_1}{\frac{1}{2} k\omega n t_1} \right) \exp\left[-ik\omega n t_1/2 \right]. \qquad (210.13)$$

The spectral amplitudes $|C_k|$ have been plotted in Fig. 2.2 for impulses of minimum duration ($n = 1$) and eight times the minimum duration ($n = 8$). The well known relation between the duration of a pulse and its Fourier spectrum is evident from Fig. 2.2, e.g., the shorter the pulse, the greater the amplitude of the high frequency terms. It should be noted that the impulse with $n = 1$ is the Fourier series approximation of a Dirac delta function.

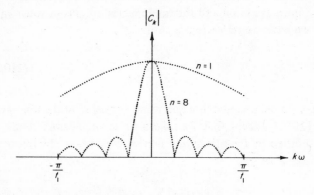

Fig. 2.2.   Spectral amplitudes for an impulse of minimum duration ($n = 1$) and eight times the minimum duration ($n = 8$).

Each point on the dotted curves in Fig. 2.2 gives a particular spectral amplitude $|C_k|$ in (210.11) and the separation of each term in (210.11) on the frequency $k\omega$ axis equals ω. The *Fourier integral* corresponds to the limiting case, in which the dotted curves $|C_k|$ (Fig. 2.2) become continuous functions of the frequency $|C(\omega)|$ by allowing the minimum time t_1 to approach zero, and the number N to approach infinity. We obtain the Fourier integral by replacing ω by $d\omega$, and, in turn, replacing $k\,d\omega$ by ω, converting (210.8) into

$$C(\omega) = (d\omega/2\pi) \int_{-\infty}^{\infty} V(t)\,e^{-i\omega t}\,dt, \qquad (210.14)$$

and then finally by taking the limit of the sum (210.11) to obtain the following integral

$$V(t) = \int_{-\infty}^{\infty} \exp[i\omega t]\, d\omega/2\pi \int_{-\infty}^{\infty} V(t') \exp[-i\omega t']\, dt'.$$
(210.15)

Among the necessary conditions on $V(t)$ are that it be sectionally continuous and single-valued, and that the integral $\int_{-\infty}^{\infty} |V(t)|\, dt$ converge. Thus, the Fourier integral provides an appropriate expression for the damped motion of a mechanical system following an impulse.

The following integral is referred to as the *Fourier transform* of the function $V(t)$.

$$v(\omega) = \int_{-\infty}^{\infty} V(t') \exp[-i\omega t']\, dt'.$$
(210.16)

Just as $2|C_k|$ gives the spectral amplitude in the Fourier series, $2|v(\omega)|$ gives the spectral amplitude per unit frequency of the Fourier integral.

Let us now determine the Fourier transform of an impulse function which is equivalent to (210.12) but expressed in a different form. By taking the Heaviside unit function

$$\begin{aligned} H(t) &= 0, && t \leqslant 0, \\ &= 1, && 0 < t, \end{aligned}$$
(210.17)

we may write the impulse function,

$$I(t) = \frac{H(t) - H(t - \Delta t)}{\Delta t} = \frac{\Delta H}{\Delta t}.$$
(210.18)

The following expression is the Fourier transform of (210.18) which may be obtained by inserting (210.18) in (210.16) and carrying out the integration.

$$i(\omega) = \left(\frac{\sin \tfrac{1}{2}\omega\, \Delta t}{\tfrac{1}{2}\omega\, \Delta t} \right) \exp[-i\omega\, \Delta t/2]$$
(210.19)

The Fourier transform of the impulse (210.19) is the same mathematical expression as (210.13), except that (210.19) gives a continuous spectrum, while (210.13) gives the distribution of discrete points.

If we take the limit of (210.18)

$$\frac{dH}{dt} = \lim_{\Delta t \to 0} \frac{\Delta H}{\Delta t} = \lim_{\Delta t \to 0} I(t), \tag{210.20}$$

then we have

$$\int_0^\infty \frac{dH}{dt}\, dt = 1,$$

and   (210.21)

$$\frac{dH}{dt} = 0, \qquad \text{for } t \neq 0.$$

Therefore, as (210.21) is Dirac's definition of the delta function, that function may be represented by the relation

$$\delta(t) = dH/dt. \tag{210.22}$$

The following quotation by Maxwell (1877) indicates that our terminology does not do justice to the history of the function (210.22). "The smaller we suppose the increment of time δt, the greater must be the impressed forces, but the time-integral, or impulse, of each force will remain finite. The limiting value of the impulse, when the time is diminished and ultimately vanishes, is defined as the *instantaneous impulse*"; Reading further, one finds that Maxwell employed the limit of the impulse function (210.18) in essentially the same way that it is employed here and in subsequent chapters. Actually, one finds the "delta" function used even a centutry before Dirac's time by Cauchy (1815, 1816) and Poisson (1816).

By taking the corresponding limit of (210.19) the Fourier transform of the delta function $\Delta(\omega)$ may be obtained with the following well known result.

$$\Delta(\omega) = \lim_{\Delta t \to 0} i(\omega) = 1. \tag{210.23}$$

Consider the square magnitude of the series given by (210.11), which may be written

$$|F(t)|^2 = \sum_{-N/2}^{N/2} \sum_{-N/2}^{N/2} C_k C_{k'}^* \exp\left[i(k-k')\omega t\right]. \qquad (210.24)$$

By integrating (210.24) over a period, one obtains the expression

$$\int_{-T/2}^{T/2} |F(t)|^2 \, dt = T \sum_{-N/2}^{N/2} |C_k|^2. \qquad (210.25)$$

By dividing (210.25) through by the period T, one can obtain the mean square

$$\overline{|F(t)|^2} = \frac{1}{T} \int_{-T/2}^{T/2} |F(t)|^2 \, dt = \sum_{-N/2}^{N/2} |C_k|^2. \qquad (210.26)$$

Hence, (210.26) indicates that the mean square of the function $|F(t)|^2$ is equal to the sum of the squares of its spectral amplitudes. To obtain the corresponding expression for the Fourier integral, let us now take the limit of the sum in (210.26) by replacing $2\pi/T$ by $d\omega$, $k\omega$ by ω, C_k by $C(\omega)\,d\omega/2\pi$, and the summation by an integration. Thus we obtain the statement of a theorem

$$\int_{-\infty}^{\infty} |F(t)|^2 \, dt = (1/2\pi) \int_{-\infty}^{\infty} |C(\omega)|^2 \, d\omega, \quad (210.27)$$

which has been attributed variously to Parseval and Lord Rayleigh.

It should be pointed out that an actual physical impulse can be described only by the impulse function $I(t)$ as given by (210.12) with t_1 finite, or by (210.18) with Δt finite, and not by the Dirac delta function $\delta(t)$. Although a delta function impulse cannot be realized physically, its mathematical use to obtain the response of a physical system to an impulse has wide applicability. However, it is unsafe to employ the Dirac delta function indiscriminately. For example, the integral $\int_{-\infty}^{\infty} |I(t)|^2 \, dt$ converges as long as Δt is finite, but it follows from (210.27) that the integral $\int_{-\infty}^{\infty} |\delta(t)|^2 \, dt$ is divergent. This divergence comes about through the inevitable relation between the duration of a pulse and the width of its spectrum, a subject which is discussed in Chapter 6, Section 6.1.2. It is hardly necessary to add that the various properties of the Dirac delta function have been treated extensively elsewhere.

There are several ways in which the Fourier integral may be extended to include a wider class of functions, and a method which has been widely adopted will now be discussed. It is referred to variously as the generalized *Fourier integral*, and the *Laplace transform*. However, it closely resembles the operational calculus of Heaviside whose work stimulated the development of the Laplace transform.

The transform method will be used only with functions which vanish before time $t = 0$, i.e., only functions written $F(t) = 0$, $t < 0$ are considered. This requirement may be met by multiplying any arbitrary function $P(t)$ by the Heaviside unit function $H(t)$, e.g., $F(t) = P(t)H(t)$. In this case, the limits of integration for the Fourier transform are 0 and ∞ rather than $-\infty$ and ∞, e.g.,

$$f(\omega) = \int_0^\infty e^{-i\omega t} F(t) \, dt. \tag{210.28}$$

We now replace $i\omega$ by ζ, which may be complex, to obtain the following more general transform

$$f(\zeta) = \int_0^\infty e^{-\zeta t} F(t) \, dt. \tag{210.29}$$

We sometimes prefer to write the transform of $F(t)$ as $\Xi F(t)$ instead of $f(\zeta)$, and we often refer to $F(t)$ as the inverse transform of $f(\zeta)$. When ζ reduces to $i\omega$, (210.29) gives the Fourier transform as a special case.

Among the conditions on $F(t)$ are that it be sectionally continuous and that the integral (210.29) converge to form an analytic function $f(\zeta)$. It may be shown that if

$$|F(t)| < Me^{at} \tag{210.30}$$

with M a constant, and with $a < \mathrm{Re}\,\zeta$, then the integral $f(\zeta)$ converges and is an analytic function of ζ in the half plane $a < \mathrm{Re}\,\zeta$.

The following expression for the transform of the derivative of a function $F(t)$ may be obtained through the process of integration by parts.

$$\Xi\frac{dF}{dt} = \int_0^\infty e^{-\zeta t}\frac{dF}{dt}\,dt = e^{-\zeta t}F(t)\Big|_0^\infty + \zeta\int_0^\infty e^{-\zeta t}F(t)\,dt, \tag{210.31}$$

therefore

$$\Xi\frac{dF}{dt} = \zeta\,\Xi\,F(t) - F(0). \tag{210.32}$$

Similarly, the transform for the second derivative may be written

$$\Xi\frac{d^2F}{dt^2} = \zeta\,\Xi\frac{dF}{dt} - \left(\frac{dF}{dt}\right)_{t=0}. \tag{210.33}$$

By inserting (210.32) into (210.33), one obtains the expression

$$\Xi\frac{d^2F}{dt^2} = \zeta^2\,\Xi\,F(t) - \zeta F(0) - \left(\frac{dF}{dt}\right)_{t=0}. \tag{210.34}$$

By extending steps (210.32) to (210.33), and (210.33) to (210.34), it follows by induction that the transform of the nth derivative may be written

$$\Xi\frac{d^nF}{dt^n} = \zeta^n\,\Xi\,F(t) - \zeta^{n-1}F(0)$$
$$- \zeta^{n-2}\left(\frac{dF}{dt}\right)_{t=0}\cdots\left(\frac{d^{n-1}F}{dt^{n-1}}\right)_{t=0}. \tag{210.35}$$

Furthermore, it follows from (210.32) that

$$\Xi F(t) = \zeta \, \Xi \int_0^t F(\tau) \, d\tau - \int_0^{t=0} F(\tau) \, d\tau . \qquad (210.36)$$

The second term on the right-hand side of (210.36) vanishes, and, by dividing both sides of that equation by ζ, one obtains the transform of the integral of the function, e.g.,

$$\Xi \int_0^t F(\tau) \, d\tau = \frac{1}{\zeta} \, \Xi F(t) . \qquad (210.37)$$

The method of solving linear differential equations by transforms will be briefly outlined; the method will be illustrated in detail later. Consider a linear differential equation which has as its solution a function $F(t)$. The equation is multiplied through by the factor $e^{-\zeta t}$ and integrated over the limits 0 to ∞. The resulting expression may be solved for the transform of the solution $f(\zeta)$, and the solution $F(t)$ may then be determined from $f(\zeta)$ by any one of several methods. Just as (210.16) was extended to form (210.29), it is possible to extend (210.15) to yield the following relation

$$F(t) = (1/2\pi i) \int_{\gamma - i\omega}^{\gamma + i\omega} e^{\zeta t} f(\zeta) \, d\zeta \qquad (210.38)$$

in which γ is more positive than the real component of any pole of $f(\zeta)$. The solution of the differential equation may be obtained by performing the integration indicated in (210.38). It is frequently the case that $F(t)$ may be determined with less labor by rearranging $f(\zeta)$ to assume a familiar form that reveals the solution either by inspection immediately, or after referring to a table of transforms. It is necessary to acquire a familiarity with the transforms of common functions in order to solve differential equations by the transform method with any degree of facility.

We have for the transforms of the delta and unit functions

$$\Xi \, \delta(t) = \int_0^\infty \delta(t) \, e^{-\zeta t} \, dt = 1 \,, \qquad (210.39)$$

and

$$\Xi \, H(t) = \int_0^\infty H(t) \, e^{-\zeta t} \, dt = 1/\zeta \,. \qquad (210.40)$$

Rather than carrying out the integration indicated in (210.40), its transform may be obtained immediately by dividing (210.39) by ζ, a step which follows from (210.22) and (210.37).

Some common functions and their Laplace transforms are listed in Table 2.1.

TABLE 2.1

SOME COMMON FUNCTIONS AND THEIR LAPLACE TRANSFORMS

$f(\zeta)$	$F(t)$
$\zeta^{-n}, \quad n = 1, 2, 3,\dots$	$\dfrac{t^{n-1}}{(n-1)!}$
$(\zeta - \alpha)^{-1}$	$e^{\alpha t}$
$\alpha/(\zeta^2 - \alpha^2)$	$\sinh \alpha t$
$\zeta/(\zeta^2 - \alpha^2)$	$\cosh \alpha t$
$\omega/(\zeta^2 + \omega^2)$	$\sin \omega t$
$\zeta/(\zeta^2 + \omega^2)$	$\cos \omega t$
$\zeta^{-1/2}$	$(\pi t)^{-1/2}$

Several general relations are considered next. First we consider Heaviside's Shifting Theorem, which concerns a function $V(t)H(t)$, for which the transform is $v(\zeta)$. When the appearance of the function is delayed in time so that it is transformed from $V(t)H(t)$ to $V(t - \tau)H(t - \tau)$, with τ a constant, then the transform is given according to Heaviside's shifting theorem by the following expression

$$\Xi \, V(t - \tau) \, H(t - \tau) = e^{-\zeta \tau} v(\zeta) \,. \qquad (210.41)$$

In those cases for which the integral $\int_{-\infty}^\infty |V(t)| \, dt$ converges, ζ may be replaced simply by $i\omega$, and we may write Heaviside's shifting theorem as

$$\Xi\, V(t - \tau) H(t - \tau) = e^{-i\omega\tau} v(i\omega), \qquad (210.42)$$

we see that the time delay corresponds to the delay in phase by $-\omega\tau$. Thus, as might be expected, the spectrum of the pulse $V(t-\tau)H(t-\tau)$ is the same as that of $V(t)H(t)$ except for the phase factor $e^{-i\omega\tau}$.

The following general relation gives the transform of a function having an exponential factor. If a function $V(t)$ has the transform $v(\zeta)$, it may be easily shown that the transform of the product $e^{\alpha t} V(t)$ is given by the following expression.

$$\Xi\, e^{\alpha t} V(t) = v(\zeta - \alpha). \qquad (210.43)$$

There are some special cases of (210.43) that provide important physical relations; e.g., consider a function $V(t)$ which may be expressed by a Fourier integral so that ζ may be replaced simply by $i\omega$. In this case, the transform of the product $e^{i\omega_0 t} V(t)$ may be written

$$\Xi\, e^{i\omega_0 t} V(t) = v(i\omega - i\omega_0), \qquad (210.44)$$

which is the same as the spectrum of the pulse $V(t)$ except that it has been displaced along the frequency axis by the amount ω_0. Hence, it follows by (210.44) that to convert a nonconverging monochromatic factor $e^{i\omega_0 t}$ to one that converges by multiplying it by $V(t)$, the resulting convergent expression cannot be monochromatic but must have the same spectral width as that of the function $V(t)$.

As an example, take a sinusoidal wave train of constant amplitude but finite duration Δt, which is given by letting $V(t)$ represent the impulse function $I(t)$, stated by (210.18). It follows by (210.19) and (210.44) that this wave train has the Fourier transform

$$\Xi\, \exp[i\omega_0 t]\, I(t) = \left(\frac{\sin(\omega - \omega_0)\,\Delta t/2}{(\omega - \omega_0)\,\Delta t/2}\right) \exp[-i(\omega - \omega_0)\,\Delta t/2],$$

$$(210.45)$$

which clearly indicates that the spectral width of the wave train is the same as that of the impulse function, viz. (210.19), which becomes more narrow with increasing duration Δt.

As another example, take a sinusoidal wave train which decays exponentially with time as indicated by letting $V(t)$ represent $e^{-\alpha t}$ in (210.44). It follows by (210.44) and Table 2.1 that the exponentially damped wave train has the transform

$$\varXi \exp\left[(i\omega_0 - \alpha)t\right] = \{\alpha + i(\omega - \omega_0)\}^{-1}, \qquad (210.46)$$

which is the well-known dispersion relation. The square of the spectral amplitude $[\alpha^2 + (\omega - \omega_0)^2]^{-1}$ is within half of its maximum value over a frequency interval of 2α, which is sometimes referred to as the *Lorentz line width*.

By letting at replace t in (210.29), one may easily obtain the following relation

$$\varXi V(at) = (1/a)v(\zeta/a), \qquad (210.47)$$

which is particularly useful in dealing with the generalized transform. The special case of the Fourier transform

$$\varXi V(at) = (1/a)v(i\omega/a), \qquad (210.48)$$

clearly illustrates the relation between the time of an event and its spectrum; viz. (210.48) shows that multiplying the time of an event by the factor a divides both the spectral width and amplitude by the same factor.

The *convolution* of the two functions $V_1(t)$ and $V_2(t)$, written

$$V_1 V_2(t) = \int_0^t V_1(t - \tau) V_2(\tau) \, d\tau, \qquad (210.49)$$

is known variously as the *convolution integral* and the *faltung integral*, and it plays an important role in the solution of differential equations by the transform method. It may be shown that the convolution of two functions is symmetric, i.e., the convolution $V_1 V_2(t)$ equals the convolution $V_2 V_1(t)$, and it may be shown also that the convolution has the following transform

$$\varXi\, V_1 V_2(t) = v_1(\zeta) v_2(\zeta). \tag{210.50}$$

If one seeks the inverse transform of a product $v_1(\zeta) v_2(\zeta)$, it is often preferable to determine the inverse transforms of the two factors separately, and then take the convolution of the two according to (210.49).

We now consider the solution of a system of simultaneous linear differential equations by the transform method, the representative equations being given by the general expression

$$S_{ij} F_j(t) = J_i(t), \tag{210.51}$$

in which the elements of the secular matrix are the differential operators

$$S_{ij} = a_{ij} \frac{d^2}{dt^2} + b_{ij} \frac{d}{dt} + c_{ij}, \tag{210.52}$$

and the functions $J_i(t)$ are known, while the functions $F_j(t)$ are to be determined. We now multiply both sides of (210.51) by the factor $e^{-\zeta t}$ and integrate over the limits 0 to ∞. The resulting expression may be written

$$s_{ij}(\zeta) f_j(\zeta) = j_i(\zeta) + p_i(\zeta, F_j(0), F_j'(0), \ldots), \tag{210.53}$$

in which the elements of the new secular matrix are given by the expression

$$s_{ij}(\zeta) = a_{ij} \zeta^2 + b_{ij} \zeta + c_{ij}, \tag{210.54}$$

and $j_i(\zeta)$ and $f_j(\zeta)$ are the transforms of the given functions and the functions to be determined respectively, i.e.,

$$\varXi\, J_i(t) = j_i(\zeta), \tag{210.55}$$

and

$$\Xi \, F_j(t) = f_j(\zeta).$$

(210.56)

The term on the right-hand side in (210.53) comes entirely from the terms in (210.35) which depend on the initial conditions. It has the property that if the functions $F_j(t)$ and all their derivatives vanish initially, at time $t = 0$, then $p_i(\zeta \, F_j(0), \, F_j'(0),...)$ must vanish also. Let the inverse transforms of the functions $p_i(\zeta, \, F_j(0), \, F_j'(0),...)$ be denoted as $P_i(t)$, so that

$$\Xi \, P_i(t) = p_i(\zeta, \, F_j(0), \, F_j'(0),...).$$

(210.57)

Furthermore, let $\sigma_{jk}(\zeta)$ represent the matrix which is the reciprocal of the secular matrix $s_{ij}(\zeta)$, i.e.,

$$\sigma_{jk}(\zeta) \, s_{ki}(\zeta) = \delta_{ji}.$$

(210.58)

We now solve (210.53) for the transform of the solution by multiplying both sides of (210.53) on the left by the square matrix $\sigma_{jk}(\zeta)$ to obtain the penultimate expression

$$f_j(\zeta) = \sigma_{jk}(\zeta) j_k(\zeta) + \sigma_{jk}(\zeta) p_k(\zeta, \, F_j(0), \, F_j'(0),...).$$

(210.59)

Now let $\Sigma_{jk}(t)$ denote the inverse transform of the corresponding element of the reciprocal matrix, viz.

$$\Xi \, \Sigma_{jk}(t) = \sigma_{jk}(\zeta).$$

(210.60)

The functions $\Sigma_{jk}(t)$ are called the *Green's functions* of the system of equations (210.51). We now use relation (210.50) and obtain the final solution as the sum of two convolutions

$$F_j(t) = \int_0^t \Sigma_{jk}(t - \tau) J_k(\tau) \, d\tau + \int_0^t \Sigma_{jk}(t - \tau) P_k(\tau) \, d\tau.$$

(210.61)

Let us consider only that part of the solution given by the integral on the right-hand side in (210.61). The transform of this part of the solution may contain terms of the form

$$f(\zeta) = p(\zeta)/s(\zeta). \tag{210.62}$$

It follows from (210.35) that $p(\zeta)$ is of lower degree than $s(\zeta)$. One may expand $f(\zeta)$ by the theory of partial fractions, which indicates that there is a fraction with a constant numerator corresponding to each linear factor of $s(\zeta)$, and a fraction with a linear numerator corresponding to each quadratic factor of $s(\zeta)$, etc. Take as an example

$$f(\zeta) = \{(\zeta + 1)^2 (\zeta^2 + 4)\}^{-1}, \tag{210.63}$$

which may be expanded by the theory of partial fractions to yield the expression

$$f(\zeta) = \frac{2}{25}\left(\frac{1}{\zeta + 1} + \frac{5}{2(\zeta + 1)^2} - \frac{\zeta}{\zeta^2 + 4} - \frac{3}{2(\zeta^2 + 4)}\right). \tag{210.64}$$

Taking the inverse transform of (210.64) term by term one obtains the following solution

$$F(t) = (2/25)(e^{-t} + \tfrac{5}{2}te^{-t} - \cos 2t - \tfrac{3}{4}\sin 2t). \tag{210.65}$$

If the roots of the polynomial $s(\zeta)$ in (210.62) are distinct, e.g.,

$$s(\zeta) = (\zeta - a_1)(\zeta - a_2)\ldots(\zeta - a_n), \tag{210.66}$$

then Heaviside's expansion theorem applies and we may write immediately

$$f(\zeta) = \frac{A_1}{\zeta - a_1} + \frac{A_2}{\zeta - a_2} + \cdots + \frac{A_n}{\zeta - a_n}, \tag{210.67}$$

in which the constants $A_1, A_2, \ldots, A_n$ are given by the formula

$$A_i = \left(p(\zeta) \middle/ \frac{ds}{d\zeta}\right)_{\zeta = a_i}. \tag{210.68}$$

To prove relation (210.68), we note that A_i is the residue of $f(\zeta)$ at the pole a_i. Hence, we have

$$A_i = \lim_{\zeta \to a_i} (\zeta - a_i) \{p(\zeta)/s(\zeta)\}, \qquad (210.69)$$

which reduces to (210.68) by L'Hôpital's rule.

2.1.1. Some Relations between Real and Complex Functions

In physical problems, we often use complex series to represent generalized coordinates, their time derivatives, and forces, with the understanding that only the real parts of the expressions are to be taken into account. This practice is particularly convenient in dealing with linear functions of the coordinates and their time derivatives, because the solutions are linear superpositions of real and imaginary terms, the real terms being the same as those obtained by dealing only with real functions. This is no longer the case in dealing with powers and cross products of the coordinates and their time derivatives, as may be illustrated by the following simple example. Taking the simple expression $y(t) = y_0 e^{i\omega t}$, we have $\operatorname{Re} y\dot{y} = -\omega y_0{}^2 \sin 2\omega t$, and $(\operatorname{Re} y)(\operatorname{Re} \dot{y}) = \frac{1}{2}\omega y_0{}^2 \sin 2\omega t$. Thus in general $\operatorname{Re} y\dot{y} \neq (\operatorname{Re} y)(\operatorname{Re} \dot{y})$. However, there is a convenient method for treating the mean products of complex functions to determine the corresponding mean products of real functions. This method relies on the relations (211.5)–(211.7) which are given in the following brief development.

Consider the following complex series expansions:

$$J(t) = \sum_k J(k) \exp\left[i(\omega_k t + \alpha_k)\right], \qquad (211.1)$$

$$y(t) = \sum_k -iy(k) \exp\left[i(\omega_k t + \gamma_k)\right], \qquad (211.2)$$

$$\dot{y}(t) = \sum_k \dot{y}(k) \exp\left[i(\omega_k t + \gamma_k)\right]. \qquad (211.3)$$

The amplitudes $J(k)$, $y(k)$, and $\dot{y}(k)$ are real, with $\dot{y}(k) = \omega_k y(k)$ and $\omega_k = 2\pi k/(t_2 - t_1)$, $k = 0, \pm 1, \pm 2, \pm 3, \ldots$. The reader will find that it is rather easy to derive the following two relations.

$$\overline{[\mathrm{Re}\, J(t)][\mathrm{Re}\, \dot{y}(t)]} = \tfrac{1}{2} \sum_k J(k)\dot{y}(k) \cos(\gamma_k - \alpha_k), \qquad (211.4)$$

$$\frac{1}{t_2 - t_1} \int_{t_1}^{t_2} \frac{J(t)^* \dot{y}(t)}{2}\, dt = \tfrac{1}{2} \sum_k J(k)\dot{y}(k) \exp[i(\gamma_k - \alpha_k)]. \qquad (211.5)$$

Therefore, we have the following relation between the average product of two complex functions and the average product of the corresponding real functions.

$$\overline{[\mathrm{Re}\, J(t)][\mathrm{Re}\, \dot{y}(t)]} = \mathrm{Re}\, \frac{1}{t_2 - t_1} \int_{t_1}^{t_2} \frac{J(t)^* \dot{y}(t)}{2}\, dt. \qquad (211.6)$$

The following relation is a useful corollary to (211.6).

$$\begin{aligned}
\overline{[\mathrm{Re}\, J(t)][\mathrm{Re}\, y(t)]} &= \mathrm{Re}\, \frac{1}{t_2 - t_1} \int_{t_1}^{t_2} \frac{J(t)^* y(t)}{2}\, dt \\
&= \tfrac{1}{2} \sum_k J(k) y(k) \sin(\gamma_k - \alpha_k). \qquad (211.7)
\end{aligned}$$

Exercises

(2.1) Show that the quadratic form $(x_1 \quad x_2) \begin{pmatrix} 2 & 1 \\ 1 & 2 \end{pmatrix} \begin{pmatrix} x_1 \\ x_2 \end{pmatrix}$ in rectangular coordinates x_1 and x_2 is equivalent to the quadratic form $(y_1 \quad y_2) \begin{pmatrix} 1 & 0 \\ 0 & 3 \end{pmatrix} \begin{pmatrix} y_1 \\ y_2 \end{pmatrix}$ in the rectangular coordinates y_1 and y_2 obtained by rotating x_1 and x_2 counterclockwise through an angle $\pi/4$.

(2.2) Show that the full-wave rectified sine function is given by the following Fourier series.

$$|\sin x| = \frac{2}{\pi} \left\{ 1 - 2 \sum_{n=1}^{\infty} \frac{\cos 2nx}{4n^2 - 1} \right\}$$

(2.3) Given the Gaussian function $G(t) = \exp[-t^2/2\tau^2]/(2\pi\tau^2)^{\frac{1}{2}}$, show that its Fourier transform

$$g(\omega) = \int_0^\infty \exp[-i\omega t]\, G(t)\, dt$$

is the Gaussian function

$$g(\omega) = \exp[-\tau^2\omega^2/2].$$

(2.4) The function $V(t)$ has a Laplace transform

$$v(\zeta) = \frac{1}{(\zeta+1)(\zeta-3)} = \frac{A}{\zeta+1} + \frac{B}{\zeta-3}.$$

Show that $A = -B = -\frac{1}{4}$, and that $V(t) = [e^{3t} - e^{-t}]/4$.

(2.5) The function $I(t)$ has a Laplace transform

$$i(\zeta) = \{\zeta^2(\zeta^2+1)(\zeta^2+4)\}^{-1}.$$

Show that $I(t) = t/4 - [\sin t]/3 + [\sin 2t]/24$. Hint: In applying the theory of partial fractions it is convenient to regard $i(\zeta)$ as a function of ζ^2.

(2.6) The function $F(t)$ has a Laplace transform

$$f(\zeta) = \left\{1 + Q\left(\frac{\zeta}{\omega_0} + \frac{\omega_0}{\zeta}\right)\right\}^{-1},$$

in which $Q = \omega_0/\Delta\omega$. Show that when $Q \gg \frac{1}{2}$, $F(t)$ reduces to

$$F(t) = \Delta\omega\, e^{-(\Delta\omega)t/2}\cos\omega_0 t,$$

and when $Q = \frac{1}{2}$,

$$F(t) = \Delta\omega\, e^{-(\Delta\omega)t/2}[1 - (\Delta\omega)t/2],$$

and when $Q \ll \frac{1}{2}$, then $F(t)$ reduces to

$$F(t) = \Delta\omega\, e^{-(\Delta\omega)t}.$$

(2.7) Consider the following linear second-order differential equation with constant coefficients τ^{-1} and $\omega_0{}^2$, given the initial conditions $y(0) = y_0$ and $\dot{y}(0) = 0$, $t = 0$.

$$\frac{d^2y}{dt^2} + \frac{1}{\tau}\frac{dy}{dt} + \omega_0{}^2 y = 0.$$

Show that the solution is given by the following expressions.

$$y(t) = y_0 e^{-t/2\tau}(1 + t/2\tau), \qquad 2\omega_0\tau = 1.$$

$$y(t) = y_0\left\{(2\alpha\tau)^{-2} - 1\right\}^{1/2} e^{-t/2\tau}\sinh(\alpha t + \gamma), \qquad 2\omega_0\tau < 1,$$
with $\alpha = \left\{(2\tau)^{-2} - \omega_0{}^2\right\}^{1/2}$, and $\tanh\gamma = 2\alpha\tau$.

$$y(t) = y_0\left\{(2\omega\tau)^{-2} + 1\right\}^{1/2} e^{-t/2\tau}\sin(\omega t + \theta), \qquad 2\omega_0\tau > 1,$$
with $\omega = \left\{\omega_0{}^2 - (2\tau)^{-2}\right\}^{1/2}$, and $\tan\theta = 2\omega\tau$.

CHAPTER 2 BIBLIOGRAPHY

ERDELYI, A. (1962). "Operational Calculus and Generalized Functions." Holt, New York.

LANCZOS, C. (1961). "Linear Differential Operators." Van Nostrand, New York.

MATHEWS, J., and WALKER, R. L. (1964). "Mathematical Methods of Physics." Benjamin, New York.

YEFIMOV, N. V. (1964). "Quadratic Forms and Matrices." Academic Press, New York.

CHAPTER 3

Hamilton's Solution of
the Isoperimetrical Problem

The purpose of this chapter is to establish a logical foundation for the remaining chapters. Hamilton's principle is reviewed initially as a mathematical formulation not necessarily in connection with any physical system. Later, by interpreting Hamilton's principle through an axiom and a postulate that are both fairly self evident, two central theorems are obtained which possess wide physical significance.

3.0.   The One-Dimensional Solution

Hamilton proposed a statement of the isoperimetrical problem, and by specifying only a minimum of details, he arrived at a result which is very general. He applied the calculus of variations to determine the conditions for a stationary value of the following integral

$$\mathscr{A} = \int_{t_1}^{t_2} \mathscr{L}(y, \dot{y}) \, dt, \qquad (300.1)$$

which will be referred to hereafter as the *action integral*.[†] The function $\mathscr{L}(y, \dot{y})$ is associated with a physical system whose behavior may be characterized by the coordinate $y(t)$, and its time derivative $\dot{y} = dy/dt$. It is assumed throughout the text that the Lagrangian function $\mathscr{L}$ does not depend explicitly on the time. Although y does not necessarily refer to a point in space, and $\dot{y}$ does not necessarily correspond to a velocity in the usual

---

[†] The term *action integral* has been frequently used to specify a more restricted integral which can be a special case of (300.1).

sense, the terms *displacement* and *velocity* will be applied here to y and $\dot{y}$ respectively. The stationary value of $\mathscr{A}$ is sought under the supposition that it should establish $y(t)$, the path traversed by the system between two fixed points $y(t_1)$ and $y(t_2)$. Consider a neighboring path $\overline{y(t)}$, which is slightly different from $y(t)$ except at the end points where $\overline{y(t_1)} = y(t_1)$ and $\overline{y(t_2)} = y(t_2)$. The *variation* of $y(t)$ is defined by the relation

$$\delta y = \overline{y(t)} - y(t) = \phi(t). \qquad (300.2)$$

The variation δy is an infinitesimal, which is termed a virtual change because it refers to a change which could not occur, i.e., the change made by moving the system to the corresponding point on the nearby path $\overline{y(t)}$, with the time held constant. Thus, the distinction between δy and dy is that the latter is a change in $y(t)$ from a change in t, while the former is a change in the function itself with t constant.

The conditions for the stationary value of the action integral are obtained by making its variation vanish. In taking the variation of the action integral, we note that the operators for taking the variation and for integrating commute, so that we may write

$$\delta \mathscr{A} = \delta \int_{t_1}^{t_2} \mathscr{L}(y, \dot{y})\, dt = \int_{t_1}^{t_2} \delta \mathscr{L}(y, \dot{y})\, dt. \qquad (300.3)$$

We consider both the coordinate y and the velocity $\dot{y}$ as separate variables, and obtain the variation of $\mathscr{L}$ through its partial derivatives with respect to these variables, and so we have for the first-order variation,

$$\delta \mathscr{L} = \frac{\partial \mathscr{L}}{\partial y}\, \phi + \frac{\partial \mathscr{L}}{\partial \dot{y}}\, \dot{\phi}, \qquad (300.4)$$

and for the first-order variation of $\mathscr{A}$

$$\delta \mathscr{A} = \int_{t_1}^{t_2} \left(\frac{\partial \mathscr{L}}{\partial y}\, \phi + \frac{\partial \mathscr{L}}{\partial \dot{y}}\, \dot{\phi} \right) dt. \qquad (300.5)$$

The second term on the right-hand side of (300.5) may be integrated by parts to eliminate $\dot{\phi}$, e.g.,

$$\int_{t_1}^{t_2} \frac{\partial \mathscr{L}}{\partial \dot{y}} \dot{\phi}\, dt = \left[\phi\left(\frac{\partial \mathscr{L}}{\partial \dot{y}}\right)\right]_{t_1}^{t_2} - \int_{t_1}^{t_2} \phi \frac{d}{dt}\left(\frac{\partial \mathscr{L}}{\partial \dot{y}}\right) dt. \quad (300.6)$$

The end points of the paths coincide for $y(t)$ and $\overline{y(t)}$, therefore $\phi(t_1)$ and $\phi(t_2)$ vanish, and (300.6) reduces to the expression

$$\int_{t_1}^{t_2} \frac{\partial \mathscr{L}}{\partial \dot{y}} \dot{\phi}\, dt = - \int_{t_1}^{t_2} \phi \frac{d}{dt}\left(\frac{\partial \mathscr{L}}{\partial \dot{y}}\right) dt. \quad (300.7)$$

The following expression is obtained by inserting (300.7) in (300.5).

$$\delta \mathscr{A} = \int_{t_1}^{t_2} \phi\left(\frac{\partial \mathscr{L}}{\partial y} - \frac{d}{dt}\frac{\partial \mathscr{L}}{\partial \dot{y}}\right) dt. \quad (300.8)$$

As ϕ is an arbitrary variation and therefore inherently non-vanishing, it is both a necessary and sufficient condition that $[(\partial \mathscr{L}/\partial y) - (d/dt)(\partial \mathscr{L}/\partial \dot{y})]$ vanish to make the action integral $\mathscr{A}$ assume a stationary value. Thus, by the above argument, Hamilton arrived at the following differential equation

$$\frac{\partial \mathscr{L}}{\partial y} - \frac{d}{dt}\frac{\partial \mathscr{L}}{\partial \dot{y}} = 0, \quad (300.9)$$

which had been obtained earlier from other considerations by Lagrange. The function $\mathscr{L}(y, \dot{y})$ is ordinarily referred to as the *Lagrangian*.

Clearly, the solutions of (300.9) would be applied to a system only with reservations, among which would be whether or not the stationary value of the action integral establishes a maximum, saddle point, or minimum. Some conditions which bear on the stability of systems are discussed in Chapter 4, Section 4.0.0 and Chapter 5, Section 5.1.1.

3.1. The *n*-Dimensional Solution

We now consider a more complicated system which traverses a path that can be described only by more than one coordinate. The nature of the system determines the minimum number of coordinates required to specify its position, and that minimum number is called *the number of degrees of freedom*. Frequently more coordinates are apparently involved than the minimum number, and the additional coordinates arise through conditional relationships which make some of the coordinates dependent on others. For example, forces of constraint may account for such conditional relations between certain coordinates. Attention will be given later to the handling of more than the minimum number of coordinates, and it will be assumed in this discussion that a physical system with *n* degrees of freedom is being specified by *n* independent coordinates. This system is assigned a Lagrangian function $\mathscr{L}(y_1, y_2, ..., y_n, \dot{y}_1, \dot{y}_2, ..., \dot{y}_n)$. Its path starts at the point $y_1(t_1), y_2(t_1), ..., y_n(t_1)$ and, after an interval of time $t_2 - t_1$, arrives at a point $y_1(t_2), y_2(t_2), ..., y_n(t_2)$, both these two end points being fixed. As the coordinates themselves are independent, their variations

$$\delta y_i = \overline{y_i(t)} - y_i(t) = \phi_i(t), \qquad i = 1, 2, 3, ..., n, \qquad (310.1)$$

are also independent. As before, with the one-dimensional solution, we are concerned with finding the stationary value of the action integral

$$\mathscr{A} = \int_{t_1}^{t_2} \mathscr{L}(y_1, y_2, ..., y_n, \quad \dot{y}_1, \dot{y}_2, ..., \dot{y}_n) \, dt. \qquad (310.2)$$

We proceed to obtain the stationary value, taking one step at a time, the first being to obtain the partial variation $\delta \mathscr{A}_j$ by holding the time and all the coordinates fixed except for that of $y_j(t)$ in the integrand, and obtaining the partial variation $\delta \mathscr{A}_j$ by the same procedure that was used in Section 3.0. The total variation is the sum of the partial variations

$$\delta \mathscr{A} = \sum_{j=1}^{n} \delta \mathscr{A}_j. \qquad (310.3)$$

As the coordinates $y_1, y_2, \ldots, y_n$ and their variations $\phi_1, \phi_2, \ldots,$ ϕ_n are independent, their respective partial variations $\delta \mathscr{A}_1,$ $\delta \mathscr{A}_2, \ldots, \delta \mathscr{A}_n$ are also independent, and therefore each partial variation $\delta \mathscr{A}_j$ must vanish separately in order to make $\mathscr{A}$ stationary. Hence, by extending the arguments used to obtain (300.9), we have as a necessary and sufficient condition for the action integral to be stationary that the following n differential equations be satisfied.

$$\frac{\partial \mathscr{L}}{\partial y_j} - \frac{d}{dt}\frac{\partial \mathscr{L}}{\partial \dot{y}_j} = 0, \quad j = 1, 2, 3, \ldots, n. \qquad (310.4)$$

The n differential equations given by Eq. (310.4) are called the *equations of motion of the system.*

We now combine (300.5) and (300.6) to obtain the following expression for the jth partial variation of the action integral for an n-dimensional system.

$$\delta \mathscr{A}_j = \int_{t_1}^{t_2} \left(\frac{\partial \mathscr{L}}{\partial y_i} - \frac{d}{dt}\frac{\partial \mathscr{L}}{\partial \dot{y}_i} \right) \delta y_i \, dt + \left(\delta y_i \frac{\partial \mathscr{L}}{\partial \dot{y}_i} \right)_{t_1}^{t_2}. \qquad (310.5)$$

As the integrand in the first term vanishes, we have for the sum of the variations

$$\int_{t_1}^{t_2} \delta \mathscr{L} \, dt = \left(\delta y_i \frac{\partial \mathscr{L}}{\partial \dot{y}_i} \right)_{t_1}^{t_2}. \qquad (310.6)$$

Now let

$$\delta y_i = \tau \dot{y}_i, \qquad (310.7)$$

and

$$\delta \mathscr{L} = \tau \dot{\mathscr{L}}, \qquad (310.8)$$

with τ an infinitesimal interval of time, and by inserting (310.7) and (310.8) into (310.6), we have the results

$$\tau(\mathscr{L})_{t_1}^{t_2} = \tau\left(\frac{\partial \mathscr{L}}{\partial \dot{y}_i}\,\dot{y}_i\right)_{t_1}^{t_2}, \qquad (310.9)$$

and

$$\frac{\partial \mathscr{L}}{\partial \dot{y}_i}\,\dot{y}_i - \mathscr{L} = \mathscr{H} = \text{const}. \qquad (310.10)$$

Although (310.10) is a constant, its dependence on y_i and $\partial \mathscr{L}/\partial \dot{y}_i$ has been widely employed in analytical mechanics, and it is called the Hamiltonian function $\mathscr{H}$. In a number of special cases which are discussed later, Eq. (310.10) expresses the conservation of energy.

Let us both review and categorize the main points which have been treated in this and the preceding section.

The following axiom is implicit in both (300.1) and (310.2).

Axiom I: The behavior of physical systems may be described by functions of coordinates $y_1, y_2, \ldots, y_n$, time derivatives $\dot{y}_1$, $\dot{y}_2, \ldots, \dot{y}_n$, and the time t.

Axiom I, *which leaves the nature of the coordinates unspecified*, is essentially an affirmation of faith in a consistent pattern of Nature, and its acceptance seems necessary if indeed the term *Science* has meaning. For the most part, the coordinates y_1, $y_2, \ldots, y_n$ will be treated here without recourse to new concepts of the twentieth century, and unless otherwise stated, time will be considered invariant under a transformation of coordinates.

The following postulate is also implicit in both (300.1) and (310.2).

Postulate I: To each physical system a function $\mathscr{L}(y_1, y_2, \ldots, y_n, \dot{y}_1, \dot{y}_2, \ldots, \dot{y}_n)$ may be assigned, and the behavior of the system conforms to a stationary value of the integral

$$\mathscr{A} = \int_{t_1}^{t_2} \mathscr{L}(y_1, y_2, \ldots, y_n, \quad \dot{y}_1, \dot{y}_2, \ldots, \dot{y}_n)\, dt, \qquad (310.11)$$

over an interval of time $t_2 - t_1$, with $y_1(t_1)$, $y_2(t_1),..., y_n(t_1)$ the initial and $y_1(t_2)$, $y_2(t_2),..., y_n(t_2)$ the final configurations of the system.

We have proved the following theorems:

Theorem I: By applying the calculus of variations to Postulate I, it follows that the appropriate Lagrangian function for a physical system must be a solution to the differential equations of motion

$$\frac{\partial \mathscr{L}}{\partial y_i} - \frac{d}{dt}\frac{\partial \mathscr{L}}{\partial \dot{y}_i} = 0 . \qquad (310.4)$$

Theorem II: It follows from Postulate I and the calculus of variations that the Lagrangian functions must obey the relation

$$\sum_i \frac{\partial \mathscr{L}}{\partial \dot{y}_i} \dot{y}_i - \mathscr{L} = \mathscr{H} = \text{const}. \qquad (310.10)$$

In the following sections the Lagrangian function, the displacement y_i, and the velocity $\dot{y}_i$, will be related to some familiar physical properties.

Exercises

(3.1) Show that $(d/dt)\delta\mathscr{L} = \delta(d\mathscr{L}/dt)$.

(3.2) Show that $\int \delta\mathscr{L}\, dt = \delta\int \mathscr{L}\, dt$.

(3.3) Given the Lagrangian function $y^2 - \dot{y}^2$, show that the action integral vanishes if the limits of integration are from 0 to π.

(3.4) Given the Lagrangian function $(y - \dot{y})^2$, show that the action integral is given by the expression

$$[y(0) - \dot{y}(0)]^2 \, (1 - e^{-2\tau})/2,$$

with the limits of integration from 0 to τ.

(3.5) Given the Lagrangian function $(y + \dot{y})^2$, show that the action integral is given by the expression

$$[y(0) + \dot{y}(0)]^2 (e^{2\tau} - 1)/2,$$

with the limits of integration from 0 to τ.

(3.6) Given the Lagrangian function $\dot{y}^2 + \dot{x}^2 - \frac{1}{2}\dot{x}\dot{y} - y^2 - x^2$, show that the coordinates have the natural frequencies $2/3\pi$ and $2/5\pi$.

CHAPTER 3 BIBLIOGRAPHY

GOLDSTEIN, H. (1950). "Classical Mechanics." Addison-Wesley, Cambridge.
LANCZOS, C. (1949). "The Variational Principles of Mechanics." Univ. of Toronto Press, Toronto.

CHAPTER 4

Conservative Systems in Dynamic Equilibrium

4.0. Physical Properties of the Lagrangian

Thus far we have discussed mechanics on general terms with what might be mistaken for a cavalier disregard of application to specific cases. However, we will arrive at applications in due course, keeping our eyes open along the way so as to see those axiomatic assumptions through which we relate the Hamiltonian and Lagrangian theorems to familiar physical properties. One more postulate is required, stated here for conservative systems, and extended in the next chapter to cover nonconservative systems.

Postulate II: The Lagrangian of an isolated conservative system is the difference between two terms, the kinetic energy $T(\dot{y}_1, \dot{y}_2, ..., \dot{y}_n, y_1, y_2, ..., y_n)$ which is related to the motion of the system, and the potential energy $U(\dot{y}_1, \dot{y}_2, ..., \dot{y}_n, y_1, y_2, ..., y_n)$ which is associated with the forces of the system, e.g.,

$$\mathscr{L} = T - U. \tag{400.0}$$

One should note that the functional forms of the kinetic and potential energy are essentially unspecified. Considering the non-restrictive nature of both postulates I and II, one could expect a wide applicability for the theorems that would issue from them. Even so, the extent of generality seems surprising, and it at least seems to be a testimonial to a fundamental pattern in Nature. We will now proceed to test the generality of our postulates and theorems.

4.0.0. Translation of Mass

> *...the first part of physical science relates to the relative position and motion of bodies.*
>
> J. C. Maxwell—*Matter and Motion*

Take a static mechanical system in which the potential energy $U(y_1, y_2, \ldots, y_n)$ depends only on the configuration. As the system is resting in a static configuration, $y_1, y_2, \ldots, y_n$, the solution of the differential equations of Theorem I is trivial and by that theorem and Postulate II we have

$$\frac{\partial \mathscr{L}}{\partial y_i} = -\frac{\partial U}{\partial y_i} = 0, \quad i = 1, 2, \ldots, n. \tag{400.1}$$

The partial derivatives $-\partial U/\partial y_i$ are, of course, the forces which may be expressed as functions of the coordinates y_i, and (400.1) states that all the forces vanish within a static system in equilibrium. We now consider a translation to a slightly different configuration, $y_1 + \delta y_1, y_2 + \delta y_2, \ldots, y_n + \delta y_n$, the translation being made so slowly that inertial effects of motion may be neglected. The variation in the Lagrangian from this translation contains no contribution to the first order, as indicated by (400.1), but it may be written to the second order as

$$\delta^2 \mathscr{L} = \frac{1}{2} \frac{\partial^2 \mathscr{L}}{\partial y_i \, \partial y_j} \delta y_i \, \delta y_j, \tag{400.2}$$

or, making use of Postulate II,

$$\delta^2 \mathscr{L} = -\delta y_i \frac{U_{ij}}{2} \delta y_j, \tag{400.3}$$

with the potential coefficients

$$U_{ij} = \frac{\partial^2 U}{\partial y_i \, \partial y_j} \tag{400.4}$$

evaluated at the equilibrium configuration.

According to (400.3), the second-order variation in the Lagrangian has a magnitude equal to the work expended in moving the system to the new configuration. It is the inherent nature of the quadratic form [see (200.1) – (200.4)] that the matrix of the potential coefficients U_{ij} must be symmetric. Hence we have from (400.3),

$$U_{ij} = U_{ji}. \tag{400.5}$$

It was pointed out earlier that a stationary action integral may yield an unstable system. We encounter the first of several criteria for the stability of a system in (400.3). If $U_{ij}\, \delta y_i\, \delta y_j$ is positive definite for all possible translations to a neighboring configuration, then the system gains potential energy by leaving the equilibrium configuration, and, if released, will move back toward that equilibrium position; such a system is stable. If the equilibrium configuration corresponds to a maximum in potential energy, then $U_{ij}\, \delta y_i\, \delta y_j$ is negative for all possible translations. For a saddle point in potential energy, $U_{ij}\, \delta y_i\, \delta y_j$ is positive for some translations and negative for others. In the former case, the equilibrium configuration is unstable because the system will lose potential energy through any departure from the equilibrium configuration and gain kinetic energy to hasten its journey. In the latter case, the system is unstable for translations in those directions for which $U_{ij}\, \delta y_i\, \delta y_j$ is negative.

We may define a physical system in a variety of ways, and we often find it advantageous not to include everything acting within the system, but to exclude certain parts which may be summarized in external forces.[†] This amounts to modifying (310.4) to give the following inhomogeneous differential equations of motion,

$$\frac{d}{dt}\frac{\partial \mathscr{L}}{\partial \dot{y}_i} - \frac{\partial \mathscr{L}}{\partial y_i} = J_i, \tag{400.6}$$

[†] A systematic rule for doing this is given in Chapter 5, Section 5.0.3 by Theorem IX (Thevenin's theorem).

in which J_i represents an external force applied along the co-ordinate

$$y_i, \quad i = 1, 2, 3, \ldots, n.$$

The system may now be moved from equilibrium to a new configuration and maintained there through the agency of the external forces J_i. Let us now take the equilibrium position as the origin of the coordinate system, and limit displacements to small values so that we may write the variation of the coordinate δy_i as the coordinate y_i itself, and we may write the following Lagrangian for the system.

$$\mathscr{L} = - y_i \frac{U_{ij}}{2} y_j. \tag{400.7}$$

Thus, the linear relation between the force J_i and the coordinates y_j,

$$U_{ij} y_j = J_i, \tag{400.8}$$

follows from (400.6) and (400.7).

Consider another special case, that of a dynamic system of free particles. The particles are free in the sense that they are noninteracting, and therefore the potential energy of the system vanishes, $U = 0$. A coordinate y_i which does not enter in the Lagrangian is said to be a *cyclic coordinate*, and in the special case under consideration all coordinates are cyclic. As the particles are free, i.e., they do not interact with each other or with external forces, so that U vanishes, it follows from Theorem I, that we may write

$$\frac{\partial T}{\partial y_i} - \frac{d}{dt} \frac{\partial T}{\partial \dot{y}_i} = 0, \quad i = 1, 2, \ldots, n. \tag{400.9}$$

Let us take as a special case which is very common, that in which the kinetic energy depends only on the velocities $\dot{y}_1, \dot{y}_2, \ldots, \dot{y}_n$.

In this case, the first term of (400.9) vanishes, and we have the following constant relationship.

$$\frac{\partial T}{\partial \dot{y}_i} = \frac{\partial \mathscr{L}}{\partial \dot{y}_i} = \text{const}. \qquad (400.10)$$

The following definition provides a physical interpretation of (400.10). The momentum associated with the coordinate y_i is given by the following relation.

$$p_i = \partial \mathscr{L}/\partial \dot{y}_i. \qquad (400.11)$$

Equation (400.10) is a statement of the conservation of momentum for a system of free particles in which the kinetic energy is independent of the coordinates, and this statement is summarized in the following.

Corollary I. It follows as a corollary to Theorem I that the momentum, as defined by (400.11), is conserved for a system of free particles if the kinetic energy is independent of the coordinates.

Let us now consider a somewhat more complicated system of particles, in which the kinetic energy $T(\dot{y}_1, \dot{y}_2, \ldots, \dot{y}_n)$ depends only on the velocities, the potential energy $U(y_1, y_2, \ldots, y_n)$ depends only on the coordinates, and the particles are subject to external forces J_i. It follows from (400.6) and (400.11) that this system is subject to the relation,

$$\dot{p}_i = J_i - \frac{\partial U}{\partial y_i}, \qquad (400.12)$$

which is a generalization of Newton's second law. It is now possible, on the basis of (400.12), to provide a physical interpretation for the derivation of (310.4). That equation comes from the vanishing of each partial variation of the action $\delta \mathscr{A}_i$, the typical expression for which is given by relation (300.8). For each partial variation there is an expression $[(\partial \mathcal{L}/\partial y_i) - (d/dt)(\partial \mathcal{L}/\partial \dot{y}_i)] \, \delta y_i$ which must vanish, in which φ_i has been replaced by the equivalent expression δy_i. Let us now recall D'Alembert's principle, in which the product of the mass and acceleration is regarded as a fictitious negative force, so that a problem in dynamics becomes formally like one in statics. In a general way the expression $[(\partial \mathcal{L}/\partial y_i) - (d/dt)(\partial \mathcal{L}/\partial \dot{y}_i)]$ is the sum of the forces associated with the y_i coordinate in the sense used by D'Alembert, and hence, the product $[(\partial \mathcal{L}/\partial y_i) - (d/dt)(\partial \mathcal{L}/\partial \dot{y}_i)] \, \delta y_i$ represents the virtual work involved in a virtual displacement δy_i. Hence, the condition that this virtual work must vanish presents a clear physical interpretation of the central requirement of Postulate I.

Take a system of masses m_i with the kinetic energy depending on the velocities according to the familiar quadratic sum

$$T = \frac{m_i}{2} \dot{y}_i^2, \qquad i = 1, 2, \ldots, n. \tag{400.13}$$

and, as each particle has three velocity components, there are three terms in (400.13) for each mass, in each of which m_i has the same value. There are no external forces on the system, the only forces being those contained in the velocity independent function $U(y_1, y_2, \ldots, y_n)$. We now make a scleronomic† translation of coordinates through the following n relations

$$y_i(x_1, x_2, \ldots, x_n), \qquad i = 1, 2, \ldots, n. \tag{400.14}$$

which express the coordinates y_i in terms of the coordinates x_i. Of course the functions given by (400.14) must be single valued, finite, continuous, and differentiable with respect to the coordi-

---

† The term *scleronomic* has the Greek roots σκληρος (hard) and νομικος (law), and in the context of mechanics it means *time independent*.

nates x_i, with a nonvanishing Jacobian $|\partial y_i/\partial x_j|$. Replacing each coordinate $y_1, y_2, \ldots, y_n$ in $U(y_1, y_2, \ldots, y_n)$ by its expression in (400.14), we obtain the equivalent expression $U(x_1, x_2, \ldots, x_n)$ in the new coordinates. The following velocity transformation between the two sets of coordinates comes immediately from (400.14)

$$\dot{y}_i = \frac{\partial y_i}{\partial x_j} \dot{x}_j, \quad i = 1, 2, \ldots, n, \quad j = 1, 2, \ldots, n. \qquad (400.15)$$

It follows from the invariance of quadratic forms under a transformation of coordinates, as discussed in Chapter 2, that (400.13) may be rewritten

$$T = \tfrac{1}{2} \dot{x}_l M_{lj} \dot{x}_j, \qquad (400.16)$$

with

$$M_{lj} = \frac{\partial y_i}{\partial x_l} m_i \frac{\partial y_i}{\partial x_j}. \qquad (400.17)$$

The matrix elements M_{lj} will be referred to here as inertial coefficients. It may be seen that the matrix of the inertial coefficients M_{lj} is congruent to the diagonal matrix m_i. Note that the inertial coefficients M_{lj} are constant, either if the coordinates are restricted to small variations about a point of equilibrium, or if the transformation (400.14) is linear; but, otherwise, M_{lj} stands for $M_{lj}(x_1, x_2, \ldots, x_n)$ as it will depend on the coordinates. Therefore, it may be seen that the simple expression (400.13), when subjected to a scleronomic translation (400.14), acquires cross products in the velocities $\dot{x}_i$ and may become dependent on the coordinates x_i.

The Lagrangian in the coordinates $x_1, x_2, \ldots, x_n$, and velocities $\dot{x}_1, \dot{x}_2, \ldots, \dot{x}_n$, may be written

$$\mathscr{L} = \dot{x}_l \frac{M_{lj}}{2} \dot{x}_j - U(x_1, x_2, \ldots, x_n). \qquad (400.18)$$

The next relations follow from Theorem II and (400.18).

$$\dot{x}_i \frac{M_{ij}}{2} \dot{x}_j + U(x_1, x_2, \ldots, x_n) = \text{const}. \qquad (400.19)$$

or, with

$$\Omega_{ij} M_{jk} = \delta_{ik}, \qquad (400.20)$$

we have

$$\mathscr{H}(x, p) = p_i \frac{\Omega_{ij}}{2} p_j + U(x_1, x_2, \ldots, x_n) \qquad (400.21)$$

$$= \text{const}.$$

The following corollary to Theorem II is a statement of the conservation of energy as established by (400.19).

Corollary II. The sum of the kinetic and potential energy is a constant for a conservative system in which the kinetic energy is a quadratic function of the velocities, and the potential energy depends only on the coordinates.

Several systems are discussed later, in Chapter 5, Section 5.0.4, in which either the kinetic or the potential energy depends on both the velocities and the coordinates. In all but one of these systems, Theorem II gives a statement of the conservation of energy.

It should be clear that the postulates, theorems, and corollaries that have been stated thus far hold for systems in which the coordinates y_i, the velocities $\dot{y}_i$, the momenta $\partial\mathscr{L}/\partial\dot{y}_i$, and forces J_i, are components of vectors. It will be shown in the next section that these coordinates, velocities, momenta, and forces may also be axial vectors (pseudovectors).

4.0.1. Rotation of a Rigid Body

...Eudoxus and Archytas had been the first originators of this far-famed and highly prized art of mechanics, which they employed as an elegant illustration of geometric truths...

Plutarch

One learns in elementary mechanics that rotary motion may be treated by analogy to motion by translation, e.g., rotation through a differential angle $d\eta$ is analogous to a linear differential displacement $d\mathbf{r}$, the angular momentum $\mathbf{f}$ is analogous to the linear momentum $\mathbf{p}$, a torque $\mathbf{K}_i$ applied about the ith axis of rotation is analogous to the force $\mathbf{F}_i$ applied in the direction of the ith coordinate, and the moments and products of inertia I_{ij} are analogous to the inertial coefficients M_{ij} discussed in the previous section. Therefore, it would appear safe to assume that these analogies would suggest how to apply Postulate II, Theorems I and II, and Corollaries I and II to the rotary motion of a rigid body. With this in mind, we tentatively write the kinetic energy as the following quadratic form,

$$T = \tfrac{1}{2} \dot{\eta}_i I_{ij} \dot{\eta}_j, \tag{401.1}$$

and assume that the potential energy may be written as a function of the coordinates $U(\eta_1, \eta_2, \eta_3)$. Then we assume that Postulate II may be applied, and that the Lagrangian for the rotary motion of a rigid body may be written

$$\mathscr{L} = \tfrac{1}{2} \dot{\eta}_i I_{ij} \dot{\eta}_j - U(\eta_1, \eta_2, \eta_3), \tag{401.2}$$

and that relation (400.11) gives the angular momentum

$$f_i = \frac{\partial \mathscr{L}}{\partial \dot{\eta}_i} = I_{ij} \dot{\eta}_j. \tag{401.3}$$

Theorem I and (400.6) give the equations of motion

$$\frac{d}{dt} \frac{\partial \mathscr{L}}{\partial \dot{\eta}_i} - \frac{\partial \mathscr{L}}{\partial \eta_i} = K_i, \tag{401.4}$$

therefore,

$$I_{ij}\ddot{\eta}_j - \frac{\partial U}{\partial \eta_i} = K_i, \qquad (401.5)$$

and Theorem II and Corollary II give the statement of the conservation of energy,

$$\tfrac{1}{2}\dot{\eta}_i I_{ij}\dot{\eta}_j + U(\eta_1, \eta_2, \eta_3) = \text{const}. \qquad (401.6)$$

In order to show where relations (401.1)–(401.6) apply, it is necessary to consider some inherent attributes of rotation as opposed to translation, and to review a few fundamentals of the mechanics of rigid body motion.[†]

Attention will be confined here to unconstrained rigid bodies. Thus, the rotary motion of each rigid body must be about its center of mass. The center of mass might possess a motion of translation, but this is neglected here as it could be treated separately by the method outlined in the previous section. The center of mass establishes the origin of a system of Cartesian coordinates y_i, $i = 1, 2, 3$. The centroid of each small mass element m_s is located by the radius vector $\mathbf{r}_s$, with coordinates $(y_1, y_2, y_3)_s$, which moves about in the coordinate system changing direction with time, although each magnitude $|\mathbf{r}_s|$ remains fixed because the body is rigid.

We have the option of operating on the coordinates with a rotation matrix, either to rotate the axes in a given direction leaving the vectors fixed, or rotating the vectors in the opposite direction and leaving the axes fixed. We elect the second option as a means of moving the position vectors of the rigid body in such a way as to describe rotary motion. We first rotate the

[†] The treatment of the mechanics of rigid bodies in this section is somewhat abridged. The well known theorems on calculating moments of inertia may be found in other texts, e.g. "Elementary Plane Rigid Dynamics," by H. W. Harkness, Academic Press, Inc., New York (1964).

vectors by operating on them with a rotation matrix $\delta_{ij} + b_{ij}$, and then rotate the vectors further with a rotation matrix $\delta_{jk} + c_{jk}$. Thus, the total change in orientation may be obtained by operating on the vectors with the following matrix product.

$$(\delta_{ij} + b_{ij})(\delta_{jk} + c_{jk}) = \delta_{ik} + b_{ik} + c_{ik} + b_{ij}c_{jk}. \tag{401.7}$$

It may be seen that the last term in the product is noncommutative, which shows that the final orientation depends on the order in which the two different rotations are carried out. On the other hand, suppose we translate the rigid body by moving its center of mass from the origin to the point located by the vector $\mathbf{r}_1$, and then to a point $\mathbf{r}_1 + \mathbf{r}_2$. As true vectors commute with respect to addition, the final location is the same as if the center of mass were moved first to the point $\mathbf{r}_2$ and then to the point $\mathbf{r}_2 + \mathbf{r}_1$. Thus, if we attempt to represent rotation about the y_1, y_2, y_3 axes by the angles η_1, η_2, η_3 respectively, treating (η_1, η_2, η_3) as a pseudovector, it is clear that we cannot assume the validity of expressions (401.1)–(401.6) purely by analogy to the corresponding expressions for motion by translation given in the previous section, because vectors and pseudovectors behave differently with respect to inversion of the coordinates (Chapter 2, Section 2.0.1) and with rotation of the coordinates as shown here.

The distinction between translation and rotation becomes less sharp if we consider only motion restricted to small amplitudes. For instance, if the elements b_{ij} and c_{jk} are small compared with unity (401.7), then the noncommuting term $b_{ij}c_{jk}$ may be neglected and the final orientation becomes independent of the order of the separate rotations.

Considering only differential rotations, it may be seen that if the rotation matrix $\delta_{jk} + c_{jk}$ is the inverse of the matrix $\delta_{ij} + b_{ij}$, i.e., a vector rotated by one is restored to its original position by the other, then (401.7) must reduce to the Kronecker delta. Thus, for a differential rotation, the inverse of the rotation matrix

$\delta_{ij} + b_{ij}$ may be written

$$(\delta_{ij} + b_{ij})^{-1} = \delta_{ij} - b_{ij}. \tag{401.8}$$

Furthermore, it is an inherent property of the rotation matrix for orthogonal coordinates that its inverse equal its own transpose (200.14). Therefore, we have

$$(\delta_{ij} + b_{ij})^* = \delta_{ij} - b_{ij}. \tag{401.9}$$

It follows from (401.9) that the differential part of the rotation matrix is skew symmetric, i.e.,

$$b_{ij}^* = -b_{ji}.$$

Since the differential rotation matrix $\delta_{ij} + b_{ij}$ operates on the components of a vector y_j converting them to $y_i + dy_i$, e.g.,

$$(\delta_{ij} + b_{ij}) y_j = y_i + dy_i, \tag{401.10}$$

it follows that the skew symmetric matrix of small elements b_{ij}, operating alone on the components of the same vector y_j, yields only the differentials dy_i, i.e.,

$$b_{ij} y_j = dy_i. \tag{401.11}$$

Let us consider three simple examples of these skew symmetric matrices. The matrix

$$\begin{pmatrix} 0 & 0 & 0 \\ 0 & 0 & -d\eta_1 \\ 0 & d\eta_1 & 0 \end{pmatrix}, \tag{401.12}$$

rotates a vector about the y_1 axis through a differential angle $d\eta_1$, the matrix

$$\begin{pmatrix} 0 & 0 & d\eta_2 \\ 0 & 0 & 0 \\ -d\eta_2 & 0 & 0 \end{pmatrix}, \tag{401.13}$$

rotates a vector about the y_2 axis through a differential angle $d\eta_2$, and the matrix

$$\begin{pmatrix} 0 & -d\eta_3 & 0 \\ d\eta_3 & 0 & 0 \\ 0 & 0 & 0 \end{pmatrix} \tag{401.14}$$

rotates a vector about the y_3 axis through a differential angle $d\eta_3$. As these differential rotations combine linearly and commute, they may be performed in any order to give the same final orientation produced by operating at once on the vector by the sum of the three matrices (401.12)–(401.14), as shown in the following expressions.

$$\begin{pmatrix} dy_1 \\ dy_2 \\ dy_3 \end{pmatrix} = \begin{pmatrix} 0 & -d\eta_3 & d\eta_2 \\ d\eta_3 & 0 & -d\eta_1 \\ -d\eta_2 & d\eta_1 & 0 \end{pmatrix} \begin{pmatrix} y_1 \\ y_2 \\ y_3 \end{pmatrix} \tag{401.15}$$

$$= \begin{pmatrix} y_3\,d\eta_2 - y_2\,d\eta_3 \\ y_1\,d\eta_3 - y_3\,d\eta_1 \\ y_2\,d\eta_1 - y_1\,d\eta_2 \end{pmatrix}. \tag{401.16}$$

If we let the differential $d\eta$ represent the following pseudovector

$$d\boldsymbol{\eta} = \begin{pmatrix} d\eta_1 \\ d\eta_2 \\ d\eta_3 \end{pmatrix}, \tag{401.17}$$

it follows from (401.16) that we may write (401.15) as the following vector cross product.

$$d\mathbf{r} = d\boldsymbol{\eta} \times \mathbf{r}. \tag{401.18}$$

Dividing both sides of (401.18) by a differential in the time dt, gives the following relation between the angular velocity $\dot{\boldsymbol{\eta}}$, a vector $\mathbf{r}$, and its time derivative $\dot{\mathbf{r}}$.

$$\dot{\mathbf{r}} = \dot{\boldsymbol{\eta}} \times \mathbf{r}. \tag{401.19}$$

Note that both pseudovectors $d\boldsymbol{\eta}$ and $\dot{\boldsymbol{\eta}}$ point in the direction of the instantaneous axis of rotation (Chapter 2, Section 2.0.1), and each may be resolved into components $(d\eta_1, d\eta_2, d\eta_3)$ and $(\dot\eta_1, \dot\eta_2, \dot\eta_3)$ along the three orthogonal axes.

The total angular momentum of a rigid body may be written as the sum of the angular momenta of its incremental parts, e.g.,

$$\mathbf{f} = \sum_s m_s \mathbf{r}_s \times \dot{\mathbf{r}}_s, \qquad (401.20)$$

and as the velocity $\dot{\mathbf{r}}_s$ may be represented by the cross product $\dot{\boldsymbol{\eta}} \times \mathbf{r}_s$ (401.20) may be rewritten in the form

$$\mathbf{f} = \sum_s m_s \mathbf{r}_s \times (\dot{\boldsymbol{\eta}} \times \mathbf{r}_s). \qquad (401.21)$$

By carrying out the operations indicated in (401.21) and collecting terms, one obtains (401.3) in which

$$I_{11} = \sum_s m_s(y_2{}^2 + y_3{}^2)_s, \qquad I_{22} = \sum_s m_s(y_3{}^2 + y_1{}^2)_s,$$

$$I_{12} = -\sum_s m_s(y_1 y_2)_s, \qquad I_{13} = -\sum_s m_s(y_1 y_3)_s, \quad \text{etc.}$$

$$(401.22)$$

In practice, the moments and products of inertia of a rigid body are unlikely to be determined by taking the sums indicated in (401.22). Instead, they are ordinarily obtained by integration, making use of the density of the body ρ as shown in the following expressions

$$I_{11} = \int_{\text{vol}} (y_2{}^2 + y_3{}^2)\rho \, dv, \qquad I_{22} = \int_{\text{vol}} (y_3{}^2 + y_1{}^2)\rho \, dv,$$

$$I_{12} = -\int_{\text{vol}} y_1 y_2 \rho \, dv, \qquad I_{13} = -\int_{\text{vol}} y_1 y_3 \rho \, dv, \quad \text{etc.}$$

$$(401.23)$$

Although (401.3) holds for the angular momentum in many familiar cases, it cannot be applied indiscriminately because the moments and products of inertia are not in general constant. For example, the coordinates in (401.22) refer to the radius vectors $\mathbf{r}_s$ which rotate about the instantaneous axis established by the direction of $\dot{\boldsymbol{\eta}}$. Thus, although $|\mathbf{r}_s| = [(y_1{}^2 + y_2{}^2 + y_3{}^2)_s]^{\frac{1}{2}}$ is constant, $(y_2{}^2 + y_3{}^2)_s$ and $(y_1 y_2)_s$, etc. in (401.22) in general are not, and depend implicitly on the time through the time dependence of the coordinates $(y_i)_s$.

If the rotation of a rigid body is limited to small angles about a position of equilibrium, then the moments and products of inertia may be considered essentially constant and (401.3) holds. Consider the case of a rigid body with its movement restricted by torsion fibers which are connected so that they are colinear with the principal axes of the body (Fig. 4.1a). The torsion fibers are drawn taught and have sufficient stiffness to restrict the angular displacement of the body to small amplitudes. Friction

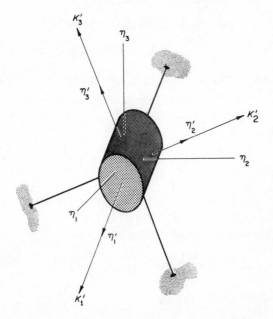

Fig. 4.1a. A rigid body supported by torsion fibers.

losses are neglected, and the dynamic equilibrium for such a body consists in stable oscillations of its own natural frequencies and those of the applied torques K_i, $i = 1, 2, 3$. The Lagrangian for this system contains a term for the kinetic energy as given already in (401.1) and has a remaining term of the general form already given by (400.7), viz. a potential $\frac{1}{2}\eta_i U_{ij}\eta_j$ based on the elastic energy of the torsion fibers.

We must account for the applied torques, and, as the torques are applied on the principal axes, we would prefer to use the components of the torques on those axes. Take K_i', $i = 1, 2, 3$, as the components of the torque applied on the principal axes, and η_i' as the components of angular displacement about the principal axes, with the two sets of coordinates related by the following scleronomic transformation

$$\eta_i = \alpha_{ij}\eta_j' . \tag{401.24}$$

We may write as the Lagrangian for the system

$$\mathscr{L} = -\tfrac{1}{2}\eta_i U_{ij}\eta_j + \tfrac{1}{2}\dot{\eta}_i I_{ij}\dot{\eta}_j . \tag{401.25}$$

Let us now make a substitution of coordinates and velocities in (401.25), using the transformation (401.24), replacing the coordinates η_i by $\alpha_{ij}\eta_j'$ and velocities $\dot{\eta}_i$ by $\alpha_{ij}\dot{\eta}_j'$, which gives the following result.

$$\mathscr{L} = -\tfrac{1}{2}\eta_i'\underbrace{\alpha_{ij}^* U_{jk}\alpha_{kl}}_{U_{il}'\delta_{il}}\eta_l' + \tfrac{1}{2}\dot{\eta}_i'\underbrace{\alpha_{ij}^* I_{jk}\alpha_{kl}}_{I_{il}'\delta_{il}}\dot{\eta}_l' . \tag{401.26}$$

As is well known, the cross product terms in the potential and kinetic energies vanish as indicated in (401.26) so that the Lagrangian may be written simply as

$$\mathscr{L} = \sum_i \left[-\tfrac{1}{2}U_{ii}'\eta_i'^2 + \tfrac{1}{2}I_{ii}'\dot{\eta}_i'^2 \right], \qquad i = 1, 2, 3 . \tag{401.27}$$

The equations of motion,

$$I_{ii}'\ddot{\eta}_i' + U_{ii}'\eta_i' = K_i', \qquad i = 1, 2, 3, \tag{401.28}$$

follow at once from (400.6) and (401.27). Equation (401.28) indicates that the system may be regarded as three force driven simple harmonic oscillators, one being associated with each of the three principal axes. Dynamic equilibrium then consists in stable oscillations at the frequencies contained in the applied torques and at the three natural frequencies,

$$\omega_i = (U'_{ii}/I'_{ii})^{\frac{1}{2}}, \qquad i = 1, 2, 3. \tag{401.29}$$

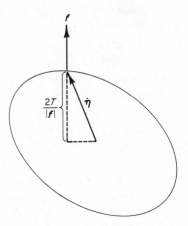

Fig. 4.1b.   Poinsot's construction.

Before considering rotation through large angles, we will take up *Poinsot's construction* (Fig. 4.1b) which provides a useful interpretation for the motion of a free rigid body subject to no torques. The physical interpretation of Poinsot's construction relies on the following relations, which come at once from (401.1), (401.3), and (401.6).

$$\dot{\boldsymbol{\eta}} \cdot \mathbf{f} = |\dot{\boldsymbol{\eta}}| |\mathbf{f}| \cos \dot{\boldsymbol{\eta}}, \mathbf{f} = 2T = \text{const}. \tag{401.30}$$

$$\mathbf{f} = \begin{pmatrix} \partial T/\partial \dot{\eta}_1 \\ \partial T/\partial \dot{\eta}_2 \\ \partial T/\partial \dot{\eta}_3 \end{pmatrix}. \tag{401.31}$$

Since kinetic energy is conserved, the ellipsoidal surface of constant energy given by (401.1) makes the angular velocity vector describe the surface of an ellipsoid. The ellipse in Fig. 4.1b represents the cross section of this ellipsoid. As the angular momentum equals the gradient of the kinetic energy in the angular velocity space, the angular momentum is normal to the surface of the ellipsoid at the point of contact of the angular velocity vector. Pointing in the same direction, the line with length $2T/|\mathbf{f}|$ remains fixed through conservation of energy and angular momentum. Thus, the motion of a free rigid body will be such as to maintain a fixed direction of the pseudovector $\mathbf{f}$ keeping the length of the line $2T/|\mathbf{f}|$ constant. If the angular velocity does not point along one of the principal axes, making the pseudovectors $\mathbf{f}$ and $\dot{\boldsymbol{\eta}}$ coincide, then the body pivots around the center of mass with the angular velocity $\dot{\boldsymbol{\eta}}$ describing a cone.

As the angular momentum and angular velocity are not in general colinear, a free unconstrained rigid body cannot rotate about an arbitrary fixed axis, as torques of constraint would be required to make the angular momentum describe a cone around the axis of rotation. Hence, a free unconstrained rigid body can have a fixed axis of rotation only around one of its principal axes. In this special case, with rotation about principal axis 1, Eqs. (401.1), (401.2), and (401.6) together yield the relation

$$\mathscr{L} = T = \tfrac{1}{2} I_{11} \dot{\eta}_1{}^2 = \text{const}. \qquad (401.32)$$

and as the coordinate η_1 is cyclic, the conservation of angular momentum

$$f_1 = \partial \mathscr{L}/\partial \dot{\eta}_1 = I_{11} \dot{\eta}_1 = \text{const}. \qquad (401.33)$$

follows from Corollary I.

There is a general method for treating the motion of a rigid body which automatically gives constant values of the moments and products of inertia. Another set of Cartesian coordinates are required which are fixed in the body, and specified as x_i,

$i = 1, 2, 3$. These are called the *body axes*, and the origin of these coordinates coincides with the origin of the coordinates y_i which we have already been considering and which will now be designated as the *space axes*. We regard the space axes as a fixed reference in which we are stationed as observers. The moments and products of inertia are specified in the body axes in which they remain constant, and for convenience with no loss of generality, we make the body axes coincide with the principal axes of the body (see Exercise 4.4).

The motion of the rigid body is taken into account through a rheonomic transformation of the body axes. There are a number of ways in which the configuration of the body axes may be specified by three independent coordinates; a common method which employs the three Euler angles will be outlined. The orientation of the Euler angles φ, θ, ψ and the corresponding angular velocities $\dot{\varphi}, \dot{\theta}, \dot{\psi}$, in relation to the position of the body axes x_1, x_2, x_3 and the space axis y_3, are shown in Fig. 4.2a. We are interested in the angular velocity components $\dot{\varepsilon}_1, \dot{\varepsilon}_2, \dot{\varepsilon}_3$ of the rigid body about the three body axes. These components comprise the pseudovector $\dot{\boldsymbol{\varepsilon}}$, and it may be seen by Fig. 4.2a that these components may be written as

$$\dot{\varepsilon}_1 = \dot{\varphi} \sin\theta \sin\psi + \dot{\theta} \cos\psi, \tag{401.34}$$

$$\dot{\varepsilon}_2 = \dot{\varphi} \sin\theta \cos\psi - \dot{\theta} \sin\psi, \tag{401.35}$$

$$\dot{\varepsilon}_3 = \dot{\varphi} \cos\theta + \dot{\psi}. \tag{401.36}$$

If we account for torques which may be expressed as functions of the Euler angles by a potential function $U(\varphi, \theta, \psi)$, then we may write the following Lagrangian for the rotary motion of a rigid body,

$$\mathscr{L} = \tfrac{1}{2}[I_1\dot{\varepsilon}_1{}^2 + I_2\dot{\varepsilon}_2{}^2 + I_3\dot{\varepsilon}_3{}^2] - U(\varphi, \theta, \psi), \tag{401.37}$$

in which the moments of inertia about the three principal axes are given by I_i, $i = 1, 2, 3$. By substituting (401.34)–(401.36) in the kinetic energy term of the Lagrangian (401.37), it may be seen that the Lagrangian is a function of the three Euler angles and their respective angular velocities, e.g.,

$$\mathscr{L} = T(\theta, \psi, \dot\varphi, \dot\theta, \dot\psi) - U(\varphi, \theta, \psi), \qquad (401.38)$$

Thus, the Lagrangian for the rotation of an unconstrained rigid body may be expressed in terms of independent coordinates in such a way that the moments of inertia remain constant. By obtaining (401.37) and (401.38) we have demonstrated implicitly that the rotation of an unconstrained rigid body may be treated by Hamilton's principle (methods of treating problems involving constraints are presented in Section 4.1).

It is convenient to use the following partial derivatives in determining the equation of motion related to the Euler angle ψ.

$$\partial\dot\varepsilon_1/\partial\psi = \dot\varphi \sin\theta \cos\psi - \dot\theta \sin\psi = \dot\varepsilon_2, \qquad (401.39)$$

$$\partial\dot\varepsilon_2/\partial\psi = -\dot\varphi \sin\theta \sin\psi - \dot\theta \cos\psi = -\dot\varepsilon_1, \qquad (401.40)$$

$$\partial\dot\varepsilon_3/\partial\dot\psi = 1. \qquad (401.41)$$

Thus, the partial derivative $\partial\mathscr{L}/\partial\psi$ may be written

$$\frac{\partial\mathscr{L}}{\partial\psi} = I_1\dot\varepsilon_1 \frac{\partial\dot\varepsilon_1}{\partial\psi} + I_2\dot\varepsilon_2 \frac{\partial\dot\varepsilon_2}{\partial\psi} - \frac{\partial U}{\partial\psi}$$

$$= (I_1 - I_2)\dot\varepsilon_1\dot\varepsilon_2 - \frac{\partial U}{\partial\psi}, \qquad (401.42)$$

so that we have for the equation of motion

$$\frac{d}{dt}\frac{\partial\mathscr{L}}{\partial\dot\psi} - \frac{\partial\mathscr{L}}{\partial\psi} = I_3\ddot\varepsilon_3 - (I_1 - I_2)\dot\varepsilon_1\dot\varepsilon_2 + \frac{\partial U}{\partial\psi} = K_3, \qquad (401.43)$$

in which K_3 represents a torque externally applied about the body axis x_3. It may be seen by (401.43) that the rotation of a rigid body is described in general by nonlinear equations of motion, the solutions of which can be very complicated. The remaining discussion will be limited to the simple case of a free rigid body, for which $\partial U / \partial \psi$ and K_3 vanish in (401.43), e.g.,

$$I_3 \ddot{\varepsilon}_3 - (I_1 - I_2) \dot{\varepsilon}_1 \dot{\varepsilon}_2 = 0. \qquad (401.44)$$

As there is nothing special about the body axis x_3, we may write the following two equations of motion by taking a cyclic permutation of indices.

$$I_1 \ddot{\varepsilon}_1 - (I_2 - I_3) \dot{\varepsilon}_2 \dot{\varepsilon}_3 = 0, \qquad (401.45)$$

$$I_2 \ddot{\varepsilon}_2 - (I_3 - I_1) \dot{\varepsilon}_3 \dot{\varepsilon}_1 = 0. \qquad (401.46)$$

Equations (401.44)–(401.46) are known as *Euler's equations of motion for a free rigid body*.

Consider the special case in which two principal moments of inertia are equal, e.g., let $I_1 = I_2$. One finds that a surprising variety of homogeneous rigid bodies may be designed to satisfy the condition $I_1 = I_2$ by employing various patterns of symmetry about the body axis x_3.[†] Of course it is also possible to design unsymmetric rigid bodies with certain peculiar features so as to make $I_1 = I_2$. In this case the second term in (401.44) vanishes, and we have immediately

$$\dot{\varepsilon}_3(t) = \text{const.} = \omega_3. \qquad (401.47)$$

Thus, if there is a component of angular velocity about the body axis x_3, it is maintained constant. If $\dot{\varepsilon}_3$ vanishes, then the second term in both (401.45) and (401.46) vanishes so that the angular velocity components about the body axes x_1 and x_2 either vanish or are constant. On the other hand, if $\dot{\varepsilon}_3$ is finite, then (401.45) and (401.46) reduce to linear equations of motion. For example,

[†] The following symmetric objects have this property: bar bell, bowling pin, discus, rolling pin, pie pan, and any other object either turned on a lathe or made on a potter's wheel.

if we divide (401.45) and (401.46) by I_1 and let

$$\omega_0 = \left(\frac{I_1 - I_3}{I_1}\right)\omega_3 \,, \tag{401.48}$$

then (401.45) and (401.46) reduce to the matrix equation

$$\begin{pmatrix} \dfrac{d}{dt} & -\omega_0 \\[2mm] \omega_0 & \dfrac{d}{dt} \end{pmatrix} \begin{pmatrix} \dot{\varepsilon}_1 \\[2mm] \dot{\varepsilon}_2 \end{pmatrix} = \begin{pmatrix} 0 \\[2mm] 0 \end{pmatrix}. \tag{401.49}$$

If we take for the boundary conditions

$$\dot{\varepsilon}_1(0) = 0 \,, \tag{401.50}$$

$$\dot{\varepsilon}_2(0) = \omega_1 \,, \tag{401.51}$$

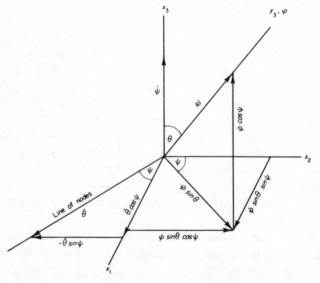

Fig. 4.2a.   The Eulerian angles shown in reference to the body axes and space axis y_3.

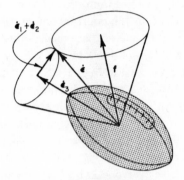

Fig. 4.2b. The rotary motion of a football after a bad kick.

we have the solution

$$\dot{\varepsilon}_1(t) = \omega_1 \sin \omega_0 t , \qquad (401.52)$$

$$\dot{\varepsilon}_2(t) = \omega_1 \cos \omega_0 t . \qquad (401.53)$$

The motion of a football will serve as an example of the case under discussion. The distortions and variations in the form of the football damp out quickly after the kick, so that it approximates a rigid body in flight over most of its trajectory. Neglecting the resistance of the air, the flight of the center of mass should describe a parabola. Superimposed on this motion by translation should be the motion about the center of mass as described by the equations of motion for a rigid body, with $I_1 = I_2$ representing the moment of inertia about an axis in the equatorial plane, and I_3 the moment of inertia about the axis of symmetry.

With a well executed punt, there will be only one component of angular velocity, viz. that about the axis of symmetry. With a well executed place kick, there will also be but one component of angular velocity, viz. about an axis in the equatorial plane, In either case, rotation is confined to one of the principal axes, the motion obeys relations (401.32) and (401.33), and the angular velocity and angular momentum are colinear.

However, the rotation of a poorly executed punt or place kick will not be confined to one of the principal axes; instead it will be described by relations (401.47)–(401.53). The main features of this solution are illustrated in Figure 4.2b. In flight, the angular momentum remains fixed and the instantaneous axis of rotation, which coincides with the angular velocity $\dot{\epsilon}$, describes a cone about the angular momentum. The components of the angular velocity about the body axes describe a second cone which maintains contact with and rolls over the surface of the first (Fig. 4.2b). Thus, as everyone knows, a football wobbles after a bad kick. The wobbling motion of a football may also be conveniently interpreted by Poinsot's construction (Fig. 4.1b).

4.0.2. Systems of Electric Charges

> ...As we shall find it necessary, in our endeavors to bring electrical phenomena within the province of dynamics, to have our dynamical ideas in a state fit for direct application to physical questions, we shall devote this chapter to an exposition of these dynamical ideas from a physical point of view...
>
> J. C. Maxwell

The foregoing postulates and theorems will now be tested on electromagnetic systems and found to apply. It will be found that, just as the theorems generated the well known laws of mechanics, here they generate well known laws of electricity and magnetism such as Kirchhoff's and Lenz's laws. We will see some of the beautiful old framework that occupied the attention of such pioneers as Helmholtz, Maxwell, and Kelvin in the theory of electricity and magnetism.

Thus far, in order to focus our attention on one thing at a time, we have considered only systems whose coordinates are of one kind, i.e., either all vectors or all pseudovectors. It is of course obvious that there are physical systems whose coordinates are mixed, some being vectors and some being pseudovectors. A new type of vector, a *charge vector*, is introduced in this section and this vector enters in the configuration of an electromagnetic system. Only those systems whose configurations depend entirely on charge vectors will be discussed in this section. Other electromagnetic systems whose configurations depend on other vectors in addition to the charge vectors will be discussed in subsequent sections. In general, the electromagnetic systems whose configurations depend only on charge vectors are those that may be treated by circuits, and indeed they represent a very large family of systems.

Consider a physical system whose configuration is given by n electrical charges $q_1, q_2, \ldots, q_n$. Here the coordinate q_i replaces the general coordinate y_i, and the electric current $\dot{q}_i$ replaces the general velocity $\dot{y}_i$. The components of electric charge q_i will be considered to comprise a charge vector. It will be found that they describe physical systems under the same sets of postulates, theorems, and corollaries as vectors and pseudovectors. Therefore as the coordinates q_i are treated formally as vectors, it seems fitting to refer to these coordinates as charge vectors, and to think of them as defining a point in *charge space*.

Consider an electrostatic system comprising n ideal (lossless) conducting bodies in an isotropic homogeneous medium with permittivity ε. This is an isolated static system, and so its Lagrangian contains neither external forces nor velocities. The Lagrangian contains only a potential energy term, which depends only on the coordinates $q_1, q_2, \ldots, q_n$. Therefore, we have the following equilibrium relations according to Theorem I,

$$\frac{d}{dt} \frac{\partial \mathscr{L}}{\partial \dot{q}_i} = 0, \tag{402.1}$$

and

$$\frac{\partial \mathscr{L}}{\partial q_i} = 0. \tag{402.2}$$

Equation (402.2) establishes the equilibrium configuration, and we let that configuration define the origin of the coordinate system. Next we apply external potentials $V_1, V_2, \ldots, V_n$ in order to make the system depart somewhat from the origin to a new configuration $q_1, q_2, \ldots, q_n$. In other words, the potential V_i has been applied to the ith body making it acquire a charge q_i, $i = 1$, $2, \ldots, q_n$. We will find in this section that the potentials V_i play the same role here as the forces J_i in Section 4.0.0 and the torques K_i in Section 4.0.1. If the electrical system under discussion falls within the scope of our postulates and theorems, then according to Postulate II and (400.7) we should have the following expression for the Lagrangian.

$$\mathscr{L} = -\tfrac{1}{2} q_i U_{ij} q_j. \tag{402.3}$$

The potential term $\tfrac{1}{2} q_i U_{ij} q_j$ gives the energy stored in the electric field within the medium surrounding the charged bodies. The following expression for the potentials follows immediately from (400.6) and (402.3).

$$V_i = U_{ij} q_j. \tag{402.4}$$

The linear relation between the potential V_i and the charges q_j as given by (402.4) is well known, and the method for determining the potential coefficients U_{ij} is ordinarily treated in intermediate texts on electricity and magnetism. The steps for calculating the coefficients U_{ij} are stated below without proof.

$$U_{ij} = \overline{(4\pi \varepsilon \, r_{ij})^{-1}}, \tag{402.5}$$

with

$$\overline{(r_{ij})^{-1}} = \overline{(\mathbf{r}_i - \mathbf{r}_j)^{-1}}$$
$$= \frac{1}{q_j} \iint\limits_{\substack{\text{integration} \\ \text{over surface} \\ \text{of } j\text{th body}}} \frac{\eta_j(\mathbf{r}_j) \, ds}{|\mathbf{r}_i - \mathbf{r}_j|}, \tag{402.6}$$

in which $\mathbf{r}_j$ is the radius vector from the origin of the space co-ordinates to some point on the surface of the jth body, and $\overline{\mathbf{r}}_i$ is the centroid of the ith body as given by the relation

$$\overline{\mathbf{r}}_i = \frac{1}{v_i} \iiint_{\substack{\text{volume} \\ \text{of } i\text{th body}}} \mathbf{r}_i \, dv, \tag{402.7}$$

with v_i the total volume of the ith body, and with

$$q_j = \iint_{\text{surface}} \eta_j(\mathbf{r}_j) \, ds \tag{402.8}$$

the charge of the jth body, with $\eta_j(\mathbf{r}_j)$ the charge per unit area of the jth body at the point on its surface given by $\mathbf{r}_j$.

The elements of the matrix which is a reciprocal of the potential coefficient matrix are the capacitances C_{ij}, i.e.,

$$C_{ij}U_{jk} = \delta_{ik}, \tag{402.9}$$

and as U_{jk} is symmetric (400.5), it follows from (402.9) that C_{ij} is symmetric.

It is possible for a *classical electromagnetic system* to remain at the origin in charge space, but still possess nonvanishing velocities in the coordinates. For example, each of the n conducting bodies may be electrically neutral with $q_1 = q_2 = \cdots = q_n = 0$ when averaged over each body, but in each body, say the ith, there may be a net migration of charge dq_i about a closed path in an interval of time dt defining a finite current $\dot{q}_i = dq_i/dt$. Taking the line integral of the magnetic vector potential $\mathbf{A}$ around this closed path gives the magnetic flux g_i enclosed by the current $\dot{q}_i$, e.g.,

$$g_i = \oint_i \mathbf{A} \cdot d\mathbf{r}. \tag{402.10}$$

We now consider a system in which $q_i = 0, \dot{q}_i \neq 0, i = 1, 2, \dots, n$. The system consists of n coils wound with ideal conducting wire and a short circuit connection is made between the two terminals of each coil. These coils are dispersed at random in a homogeneous isotropic insulating medium with permittivity ε and magnetic permeability μ. No matter how many turns there are in a coil, eq. (402.10) holds, since the path of integration must follow the conductor around every turn of the coil. It is well known that $\dot{q}_i L_{ij} \dot{q}_j / 2$ gives the energy stored in the magnetic field of such a system when L_{ij} represents the self inductance of the ith coil $(i = j)$ and the mutual inductance between the ith and jth coils $(i \neq j)$. It follows that in a system of this kind we may write

$$T = \tfrac{1}{2} \dot{q}_i L_{ij} \dot{q}_j, \tag{402.11}$$

with the kinetic energy represented by the energy stored in the magnetic field, and the inductances serving as the appropriate inertial coefficients. All coordinates in the system are cyclic and the Lagrangian is simply the kinetic energy given by (402.11). Theorem I gives the following equations of motion for the system.

$$L_{ij} \ddot{q}_j = 0. \tag{402.12}$$

It follows from (402.12), and the general definition of momentum (400.11), that each component of the momentum of this system is constant, e.g.,

$$(\text{const.})_i = L_{ij} \dot{q}_j. \tag{402.13}$$

However, we know from electromagnetic theory that (402.13) also gives the magnetic flux defined by (402.10), so that we may write

$$g_i = L_{ij} \dot{q}_j. \tag{402.14}$$

In this case the momentum g_i is connected with the motion of charge $\dot{q}_j$ rather than with the motion of mass. The elements of the inductance matrix are given by Neumann's formula.

$$L_{ij} = \frac{\mu}{4\pi} \oint_i \oint_j \frac{d\mathbf{r}_i \cdot d\mathbf{r}_j}{|\mathbf{r}_i - \mathbf{r}_j|}. \tag{402.15}$$

It follows automatically from the quadratic form of (402.11) that the inductance matrix is symmetric ($L_{ij} = L_{ji}$).

Continuing with the electromagnetic system whose Lagrangian is given by (402.11) we will consider how its velocity configuration $\dot{q}_i$ might be changed to a new set of velocities $\dot{q}_i'$ by a series of impulses Δg_i, $i = 1, 2, \ldots, n$, delivered to the system by outside forces in the form of the electromotive forces $V_i(t)$, e.g.,

$$\Delta g_i = L_{ij}(\dot{q}'_j - \dot{q}_j) = \int V_i(t)\, dt. \tag{402.16}$$

Consider the electromotive force $V_i(t)$ associated with the ith coil, as related to the electric field $\mathbf{E}$ and the vector potential $\mathbf{A}$, with those two vectors taken along the path of the conducting wires of the coils. We are at liberty to select a gauge in which the scalar potential vanishes ($\Psi = 0$) in the relation

$$-\nabla \Psi = \mathbf{E} + \dot{\mathbf{A}}, \tag{402.17}$$

so that the emf V_i is given by the following expression

$$V_i = -\oint_i \mathbf{E} \cdot d\mathbf{r} = \oint_i \dot{\mathbf{A}} \cdot d\mathbf{r}, \tag{402.18}$$

in which the path of integration is the same as that indicated in the case of (402.10). The Lagrangian of the system may be written according to Postulate II as

$$\mathscr{L} = \tfrac{1}{2}\dot{q}_i L_{ij}\dot{q}_j, \tag{402.19}$$

which, together with (400.6), gives as the following equations of motion

$$V_i(t) = L_{ij}\ddot{q}_j. \tag{402.20}$$

The equations of motion (402.20) are simply a statement of Lenz's law. It is clear from (402.16) and (402.20) that the velocity configuration of the system may be made to change at time t_1 from $\dot{q}_i$ to $\dot{q}_i'$ by imposing the set of impulses on the system $V_i(t) = \Delta g_i\,\delta(t - t_1)$ in which $\delta(t - t_1)$ is the Dirac delta function.

Let us consider very briefly a system in which all the coordinates are independent, with the potential energy being dependent only on the coordinates, and the kinetic energy only on the velocities. We have for the Lagrangian

$$\mathcal{L} = \tfrac{1}{2}\dot{q}_i L_{ij}\dot{q}_j - \tfrac{1}{2}q_i U_{ij}q_j. \tag{402.21}$$

This with Theorem II yields the relation

$$\tfrac{1}{2}\dot{q}_i L_{ij}\dot{q}_j + \tfrac{1}{2}q_i U_{ij}q_j = \text{const}. \tag{402.22}$$

which states that the energy stored in the electric and magnetic fields is constant. Let us now apply potentials $V_i(t)$ to the system. The Lagrangian (402.21) and Eq. (400.6) yield the following equations of motion

$$L_{ij}\ddot{q}_j + U_{ij}q_j - V_i = 0. \tag{402.23}$$

Equation (402.23) is a statement of Kirchhoff's law for the sum of the potential drops around the ith loop of the electrical network which describes the system. Kirchhoff's other law, which requires the continuity of charge at any branch point in a network, does not enter here, because it was originally assumed that the coordinates q_i, $i = 1, 2, \ldots, n$, were all independent. By employing both of Kirchhoff's laws, one may select any set of coordinates q_i, and, if some are dependent on others, this will be taken into account through the law that makes the sum of all currents $\dot{q}_i$ vanish at each branch point of the network. The treatment of a system in which the coordinates are not all independent is discussed in the next section.

Let us recapitulate three results to illustrate the scope of Theorem I: Newton's second law (400.12), Lenz's law (402.20), and Kirchhoff's law of voltage drops (402.23) all follow directly from that theorem.

The vectors discussed in this section and in Section 4.0.0 and 4.0.1 are listed in Table 4.1.

TABLE 4.1

DIFFERENT TYPES OF VECTORS, LISTED WITH THEIR CORRESPONDING COORDINATES, MOMENTA, AND FORCES

Type of vector	Coordinate y	Momentum $\partial \mathscr{L}/\partial \dot{y}$	External force
Vector	Displacement x	Momentum p	Force J
Pseudovector	Rotation θ	Angular momentum f	Torque K
Charge vector	Charge q	Magnetic flux g	Potential V

4.1. Dependent Coordinates

The selection of a set of coordinates y_i for a physical system is somewhat arbitrary, and frequently the coordinates which seem most fitting to assign to the problem are not all independent, some being interrelated through conditional relations. Suppose there are n coordinates y_i, $i = 1, 2, \ldots, n$, and m of these coordinates ($m < n$) are related to each other through conditional relationships of the form

$$\Lambda_j(y_1, y_2, \ldots, y_n) = 0, \quad j = 1, 2, \ldots, m < n. \quad (410.1)$$

When some of the coordinates are interrelated through expressions of the form (410.1), they are said to be connected through holonomic conditions, borrowing a term from the Greek with the roots $o\lambda o\varsigma$ (whole) and $\nu o\mu\iota\kappa o\varsigma$ (law). The following theorem applies when some of the coordinates are related through expressions of the kind indicated in (410.1).

Theorem III. The Lagrangian for a physical system may be expressed with coordinates which are not all independent, some being interrelated by conditional relationships $\Lambda_j(y_1, y_2, \dots, y_n) = 0$, $j = 1, 2, \dots, m < n$, simply by commencing the Lagrangian with the terms required by Postulate II, denoting these terms by $\mathscr{L}_0$, and adding terms to it to obtain the complete Lagrangian as indicated by the following expression.

$$\mathscr{L} = \mathscr{L}_0 + \lambda_j \Lambda_j(y_1, y_2, \dots, y_n). \tag{410.2}$$

The factors λ_j in (410.2) are referred to as Lagrangian multipliers, and the method of Lagrangian multipliers is used in the proof of Theorem III, which commences by applying Theorem I to (410.2), giving as the equations of motion

$$\frac{\partial \mathscr{L}_0}{\partial y_i} - \frac{d}{dt} \frac{\partial \mathscr{L}_0}{\partial \dot{y}_i} + \lambda_j \frac{\partial \Lambda_j}{\partial y_i} = 0. \tag{410.3}$$

It was mentioned in Section 4.0.0 that the equation of motion for each coordinate y_i represents the sum of the forces associated with that coordinate in the sense used by D'Alembert, that the product of that force and the variation in the coordinate δy_i represents a contribution to the virtual work, and that each of these contributions must vanish. The discussion in Section 4.0.0 referred to independent coordinates, and it is clear that each of the separate equations of motion had to vanish because the coordinates were independent. In the case at hand, where the coordinates are not all independent, it is still necessary for the virtual work to vanish, but there are two separate conditions under which the contributions

$$\left(\frac{\partial \mathscr{L}_0}{\partial y_i} - \frac{d}{dt} \frac{\partial \mathscr{L}_0}{\partial \dot{y}_i} + \lambda_j \frac{\partial \Lambda_j}{\partial y_i} \right) \delta y_i$$

vanish; one relates to the first m equations of motion, and the other to the remaining $n - m$ equations. The m Lagrangian multipliers λ_j are chosen to make the first m equations (410.3) vanish, and the remaining $n - m$ equations vanish because they express the forces along the $n - m$ coordinates which are independent.

It is clear from (410.3) that the terms $\lambda_j \, \partial \Lambda_j / \partial y_i$ represent forces, which are the *forces of constraint*. Each conditional equation (410.1) describes a multidimensional surface on which the configuration of the system must remain, and the system is held on these surfaces by the forces of constraint $\lambda_j \, \partial \Lambda_j / \partial y_i$.

Sometimes the forces of constraint on a system are nonintegrable so that the relations (410.1) do not exist. Such forces of constraint are termed nonholonomic and the mathematical expressions through which some of the coordinates are related to others are called nonholonomic conditions, and they take the following form.

$$\beta_j \, \delta y_j = 0 \,. \tag{410.4}$$

The complete Lagrangian cannot be written for such a system, but the system may be treated by the method of Lagrangian multipliers, by starting immediately with the following equations of motion.

$$\frac{\partial \mathscr{L}_0}{\partial y_i} - \frac{d}{dt} \frac{\partial \mathscr{L}_0}{\partial \dot{y}_i} + \lambda_j \beta_j = 0 \,. \tag{410.5}$$

Two simple examples of holonomic constraints will now be presented. The first example must be as old as the subject of mechanics itself, having occupied the attention of Galileo. It concerns a mass sliding down a frictionless inclined plane under a constant gravitational force $- m\gamma$ in the x_2 direction (Fig. 4.3). As the mass is constrained to remain on the plane we have the following equation of condition, relating the x_1 coordinate of the mass to its x_2 coordinate.

$$\Lambda(x_1, x_2) = - a x_1 + x_2 = 0 \,. \tag{410.6}$$

It follows from Theorem III and (410.6) that the Lagrangian for

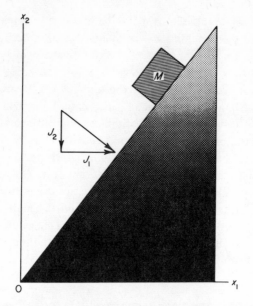

Fig. 4.3.   Mass sliding on a frictionless inclined plane.

the system may be written

$$\mathscr{L} = \tfrac{1}{2} m(\dot{x}_1{}^2 + \dot{x}_2{}^2) - m\gamma x_2 - \lambda a x_1 + \lambda x_2. \qquad (410.7)$$

The mass is to be released from rest at time $t = 0$, so that we have the boundary conditions,

$$x_i(0) = x_{i0}, \quad \text{and} \quad \dot{x}_i(0) = 0, \quad i = 1, 2. \qquad (410.8)$$

The problem posed here is to determine the coordinates x_1 and x_2 as functions of the time following the release of the mass until it arrives at the origin. By applying Theorem I to the Lagrangian (410.7) we have the following equations of motion.

$$m\ddot{x}_1 + \lambda a = 0, \qquad (410.9)$$

$$m\ddot{x}_2 + m\gamma - \lambda = 0. \qquad (410.10)$$

We eliminate the Lagrangian multiplier by solving for it in (410.9) and substituting this expression in (410.10).

$$(m/a)\ddot{x}_1 + m\ddot{x}_2 + m\gamma = 0. \qquad (410.11)$$

Then we have two equations in x_1 and x_2, (410.6) and (410.11), which, together with the boundary conditions (410.8), yield the following familiar results.

$$x_1(t) = x_{10} - \frac{a\gamma t^2}{2(1+a^2)}, \qquad (410.12)$$

$$x_2(t) = x_{20} - \frac{a^2\gamma t^2}{2(1+a^2)}. \qquad (410.13)$$

As (410.12) and (410.13) may be obtained from the most elementary considerations, we are interested here not so much in them as in the significance of the Lagrangian multiplier λ. To solve for λ, one differentiates (410.12) twice with respect to the time, and inserts the second derivative in (410.9) to obtain the following expression.

$$\lambda = -m\gamma/(1+a^2). \qquad (410.14)$$

By substituting (410.14) into (410.7), the Lagrangian then appears as

$$\mathscr{L} = \tfrac{1}{2}m(\dot{x}_1{}^2 + \dot{x}^2) - m\gamma x_2 + J_1 x_1 + J_2 x_2, \qquad (410.15)$$

in which the forces J_1 and J_2 are the forces of constraint indicated in Fig. 4.3.

Let us consider an electromagnetic system in which the coordinates are interrelated through the following holonomic relation.

$$\Lambda(q_1, q_2, q_3) = -q_1 + q_2 + q_3 = 0. \qquad (410.16)$$

Figure 4.4 is a schematic diagram of the system under consideration. All conducting bodies in the system are ideal, and they are separated by a homogeneous isotropic insulating medium with permittivity ε and permeability μ. The system is housed in a cavity, of which the walls form a conductor. As we are interested in the potential difference between the wall and each of the three large conducting bodies, we take the potential of the wall as zero for convenience. The holonomic condition (410.16) is a statement guaranteeing the over-all charge neutrality of the

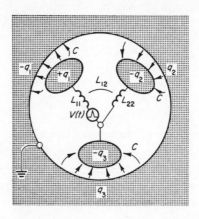

Fig. 4.4. Schematic diagram of an electromagnetic system with its charges interrelated through a holonomic condition.

system. The separation between the bodies is so great compared with the separation between each body and the wall that the electric fields that stretch between charges on the wall and on the conducting bodies dominate, and the electric fields that originate on one body and terminate on another may be neglected. The electric fields enter through the capacitances between the conducting bodies and the wall, and these capacitances are taken to be equal, each being represented by the symbol C in Fig. 4.4. The magnetic fields enter through the self inductances L_{11} and L_{22} and the mutual inductance L_{12}, and, of course, the boundary condition for the tangential component of the magnetic fields at the wall requires current flow at the interface which interacts with the magnetic fields. However, this inter-

action has no effect other than to reduce the inductances somewhat below the value that they would otherwise have if the
conducting wall were absent. Such an interaction between a
conducting wall and a coil is discussed later in Section 4.2. The
system is originally at rest at the origin of its coordinate system,
as stated by the boundary conditions

$$q_1(0) = q_2(0) = \dot{q}_1(0) = \dot{q}_2(0) = 0, \qquad (410.17)$$

$$q_3(0) = \dot{q}_3(0) = 0. \qquad (410.18)$$

The boundary conditions (410.17) are sufficient, and as the
conditions (410.18) are redundant, they have been listed separately. The system is set in motion at time $t = 0$ by an impulse
delivered by the generator connected between the central tie
point and the coil with self inductance L_{11}. It follows from
Theorem III that the Lagrangian for the system may be written

$$\mathscr{L} = \frac{L_{11}}{2} \dot{q}_1{}^2 + \frac{L_{22}}{2} \dot{q}_2{}^2 - L_{12}\dot{q}_1\dot{q}_2 - \frac{q_1{}^2}{2C} - \frac{q_2{}^2}{2C}$$
$$- \frac{q_3{}^2}{2C} - \lambda(q_1 - q_2 - q_3), \qquad (410.19)$$

and by (400.6), (410.3), and (410.19), we have the equations of
motion

$$L_{11}\ddot{q}_1 - L_{12}\ddot{q}_2 + \frac{q_1}{C} + \lambda = V(t), \qquad (410.20)$$

$$L_{22}\ddot{q}_2 - L_{12}\ddot{q}_1 + \frac{q_2}{C} - \lambda = 0, \qquad (410.21)$$

$$\frac{q_3}{C} - \lambda = 0. \qquad (410.22)$$

Next we eliminate both q_3 and λ by two substitutions; (410.16)
is substituted into (410.22) to eliminate q_3, and (410.22) is sub-

stituted into (410.20) and (410.21) to eliminate λ. The result is summarized in the following matrix equation.

$$\begin{pmatrix} \left(L_{11}\dfrac{d^2}{dt^2} + \dfrac{2}{C}\right) & -\left(L_{12}\dfrac{d^2}{dt^2} + \dfrac{1}{C}\right) \\ -\left(L_{12}\dfrac{d^2}{dt^2} + \dfrac{1}{C}\right) & \left(L_{22}\dfrac{d^2}{dt^2} + \dfrac{2}{C}\right) \end{pmatrix} \begin{pmatrix} q_1(t) \\ q_2(t) \end{pmatrix} = \begin{pmatrix} V(t) \\ 0 \end{pmatrix}. \tag{410.23}$$

The impulse which is delivered to the system by the generator to establish its motion is taken to be the fixed quantity of magnetic flux,

$$g = \int_0^\infty V(t)\,dt, \tag{410.24}$$

and in order to represent this impulse conveniently we make use of the delta function emf,

$$V(t) = g\,\delta(t). \tag{410.25}$$

The following matrix equation of the spectral amplitudes $Q_1(i\omega)$ and $Q_2(i\omega)$ is the transform of the matrix equation (410.23) of the corresponding charges $q_1(t)$ and $q_2(t)$.

$$\begin{pmatrix} \left((i\omega)^2 L_{11} + \dfrac{2}{C}\right) & -\left((i\omega)^2 L_{12} + \dfrac{1}{C}\right) \\ -\left((i\omega)^2 L_{12} + \dfrac{1}{C}\right) & \left((i\omega)^2 L_{22} + \dfrac{2}{C}\right) \end{pmatrix} \begin{pmatrix} Q_1(i\omega) \\ Q_2(i\omega) \end{pmatrix} = \begin{pmatrix} g \\ 0 \end{pmatrix}. \tag{410.26}$$

By solving (410.26) for $Q_1(i\omega)$ and $Q_2(i\omega)$, one obtains the expressions,

$$\frac{(\omega_1^2 - \omega_2^2)\,|L|\,Q_1(i\omega)}{L_{22}g} = \frac{\omega_1^2 - \omega_3^2}{(i\omega)^2 + \omega_1^2} - \frac{\omega_2^2 - \omega_3^2}{(i\omega)^2 + \omega_2^2}, \tag{410.27}$$

and

$$\frac{(\omega_1{}^2 - \omega_2{}^2)|L|Q_2(i\omega)}{L_{12}g} = \frac{\omega_1{}^2 - \omega_4{}^2}{(i\omega)^2 + \omega_1{}^2} - \frac{\omega_2{}^2 - \omega_4{}^2}{(i\omega)^2 + \omega_2{}^2},$$

with (410.28)

$$\omega_1{}^2 = (L_{11} + L_{22} - L_{12} + L_3)/|L|C, \quad (410.29)$$

$$\omega_2{}^2 = (L_{11} + L_{22} - L_{12} - L_3)/|L|C, \quad (410.30)$$

$$\omega_3{}^2 = 2/L_{22}C, \quad (410.31)$$

$$\omega_4{}^2 = 1/(L_{12}C), \quad (410.32)$$

$$|L| = L_{11}L_{22} - L_{12}^2, \quad (400.33)$$

and

$$L_3 = \{(L_{11} + L_{22} - L_{12})^2 - 3|L|\}^{\frac{1}{2}}. \quad (410.34)$$

By taking the inverse transforms of (410.27) and (410.28), the spectral amplitudes $Q_1(i\omega)$ and $Q_2(i\omega)$ are converted to the following expressions for the charges $q_1(t)$ and $q_2(t)$.

$$\omega_3 L_3 q_1(t) = g\left[\left(\frac{\omega_1}{\omega_3} - \frac{\omega_3}{\omega_1}\right)\sin \omega_1 t - \left(\frac{\omega_2}{\omega_3} - \frac{\omega_3}{\omega_2}\right)\sin \omega_2 t\right], \quad (410.35)$$

$$\omega_4 L_3 q_2(t) = g\left[\left(\frac{\omega_1}{\omega_4} - \frac{\omega_4}{\omega_1}\right)\sin \omega_1 t - \left(\frac{\omega_2}{\omega_4} - \frac{\omega_4}{\omega_2}\right)\sin \omega_2 t\right]. \quad (410.36)$$

It has been found that the system has two independent co-ordinates $q_1(t)$ and $q_2(t)$, and that in response to an impulse, the system oscillates about the origin with the natural frequencies ω_1 and ω_2.

We will now alter the electromagnetic system that was discussed above in such a way that its coordinates will be interrelated through a nonholonomic condition. This is done by removing two of the conducting bodies, and connecting the coils directly to the conducting wall as shown in Fig. 4.5. The location of the generator has been shifted, but this is an arbitrary change that has no bearing on whether the coordinates are

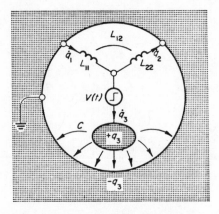

Fig. 4.5. A schematic diagram of an electromagnetic system with its charges interrelated through a nonholonomic condition.

related by holonomic or nonholonomic conditions. There is only one charge in the system, viz. q_3, that can be defined. However, not only q_3, but also the dynamic behavior of the entire system, depends on the two charging paths that carry the currents $\dot{q}_1$ and $\dot{q}_2$. According to Kirchoff's law for the summation of currents at a tie point of a circuit, the charging currents are related by the following nonholonomic condition:

$$\dot{q}_1 - \dot{q}_2 - \dot{q}_3 = 0, \qquad (410.37)$$

or

$$dq_1 - dq_2 - dq_3 = 0. \tag{410.38}$$

By comparing the system illustrated by Fig. 4.5 with the one illustrated by Fig. 4.4, one may see that there is a definite relation between the coordinates in the one example (Fig. 4.4), whereas in the other (Fig. 4.5) it is possible to state conditions only on the velocities. The system is originally at rest with $q_3(0) = 0$; it is set into motion by the generator, which delivers an emf of the form

$$V_3(t) = V_0 H(t), \tag{410.39}$$

with $H(t)$ the Heaviside unit step function (210.17). The initial velocities and accelerations corresponding to the currents $\dot{q}_1$ and $\dot{q}_2$ are stated in the boundary conditions

$$\dot{q}_1(0) = \dot{q}_2(0) = \ddot{q}_1(0) = \ddot{q}_2(0) = 0. \tag{410.40}$$

The Lagrangian of the system may be written according to Postulate II as

$$\mathscr{L} = \frac{L_{11}}{2} \dot{q}_1{}^2 + \frac{L_{22}}{2} \dot{q}_2{}^2 - L_{12} \dot{q}_1 \dot{q}_2 - \frac{q_3{}^2}{2C}, \tag{410.41}$$

and by relating (410.38) to (410.4) we may write the following equations of motion on the basis of (400.6) and (410.5)

$$L_{11} \ddot{q}_1 - L_{12} \ddot{q}_2 + \lambda = 0, \tag{410.42}$$

$$L_{22} \ddot{q}_2 - L_{12} \ddot{q}_1 - \lambda = 0, \tag{410.43}$$

$$(q_3/C) - V_3 - \lambda = 0. \tag{410.44}$$

The Lagrangian multiplier λ is now eliminated by substituting (410.44) into both (410.42) and (410.43) to give the relations

$$L_{11} \ddot{q}_1 - L_{12} \ddot{q}_2 + (q_3/C) = V_0 H(t), \tag{410.45}$$

$$L_{22} \ddot{q}_2 - L_{12} \ddot{q}_1 - (q_3/C) = -V_0 H(t). \tag{410.46}$$

We now differentiate both (410.45) and (410.46) with respect to the time and substitute (410.37) into each in order to eliminate $\dot{q}_3$. The result is the matrix equation

$$
\begin{bmatrix}
\left(L_{11}\dfrac{d^2}{dt^2}+\dfrac{1}{C}\right) & -\left(L_{12}\dfrac{d^2}{dt^2}+\dfrac{1}{C}\right) \\[2mm]
-\left(L_{12}\dfrac{d^2}{dt^2}+\dfrac{1}{C}\right) & \left(L_{22}\dfrac{d^2}{dt^2}+\dfrac{1}{C}\right)
\end{bmatrix}
\begin{bmatrix} \dot{q}_1 \\[2mm] \dot{q}_2 \end{bmatrix}
= V_0
\begin{bmatrix} \delta(t) \\[2mm] -\delta(t) \end{bmatrix}.
\tag{410.47}
$$

Taking the transform of (410.47), one can obtain as the matrix equation of the corresponding spectral amplitudes,

$$
\begin{bmatrix}
\left((i\omega)^2 L_{11}+\dfrac{1}{C}\right) & -\left((i\omega)^2 L_{12}+\dfrac{1}{C}\right) \\[2mm]
-\left((i\omega)^2 L_{12}+\dfrac{1}{C}\right) & \left((i\omega)^2 L_{22}+\dfrac{1}{C}\right)
\end{bmatrix}
\begin{bmatrix} \dot{Q}_1(i\omega) \\[2mm] \dot{Q}_2(i\omega) \end{bmatrix}
=
\begin{bmatrix} V_0 \\[2mm] -V_0 \end{bmatrix},
\tag{410.48}
$$

in which $\dot{Q}_1(i\omega)$ and $\dot{Q}_2(i\omega)$ represent the spectral amplitudes of $\dot{q}_1(t)$ and $\dot{q}_2(t)$ respectively. By solving (410.48) for the spectral amplitudes, and taking the inverse transforms, the velocities are obtained, viz.

$$
\dot{q}_1(t) = \left(\frac{L_{22}-L_{12}}{L_{11}+L_{22}-2L_{12}}\right)\omega_0 C V_0 \sin\omega_0 t,
\tag{410.49}
$$

and

$$
\dot{q}_2(t) = -\left(\frac{L_{11}-L_{12}}{L_{11}+L_{22}-2L_{12}}\right)\omega_0 C V_0 \sin\omega_0 t,
\tag{410.50}
$$

with

$$
\omega_0{}^2 = (L_0 C)^{-1},
\tag{410.51}
$$

in which

$$
L_0 = \frac{L_{11}L_{22}-L_{12}^2}{L_{11}+L_{22}-2L_{12}}
\tag{410.52}
$$

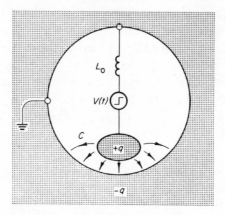

Fig. 4.6.   An *LC* simple harmonic oscillator.

gives the inductance of the two coupled coils connected in parallel. As the solution for the current $\dot{q}_2$ is negative (410.50), it flows in the direction opposite to that indicated in Figure 4.5. The solution indicates that the behavior of the charged body would be the same if the two coils were replaced by one coil as shown in Fig. 4.6 with its self inductance L_0 satisfying the relation (410.52). Note that the dynamic behavior of the system is like that of a simple harmonic oscillator with one time dependent coordinate; this could have been anticipated at the beginning of the problem by noting from (410.41) that there is only one noncyclic coordinate. Not only in this example but in all electromagnetic systems having nonholonomic conditions, these conditions are a statement of Kirchhoff's law for the summation of currents at all junction points in the system.

4.2.   Examples

Consider the dynamic behavior of two point masses moving

about their common center of mass under the gravitational force of attraction between them.[†] The coordinates of the two masses in their orbital plane consist respectively of two radial coordinates r_1 and r_2 and two polar angles θ_1 and θ_2. The masses are designated respectively as m_1 and m_2, and the origin of the coordinate system is located at the center of mass. We have for the potential energy from gravitational attraction

$$U = - \frac{U_0 r_0}{r_1 + r_2}, \qquad (420.1)$$

in which U_0 and r_0 are constants. The kinetic energy,

$$T = \tfrac{1}{2} m_1 \dot{r}_1{}^2 + \tfrac{1}{2} m_1 (r_1 \dot{\theta}_1)^2 + \tfrac{1}{2} m_2 \dot{r}_2{}^2 + \tfrac{1}{2} m_2 (r_2 \dot{\theta}_2)^2, \qquad (420.2)$$

depends not only on the time derivates of all the coordinates, but also on the radial coordinates. According to Postulate II we have for the Lagrangian

$$\mathscr{L} = \tfrac{1}{2} m_1 \dot{r}_1{}^2 + \tfrac{1}{2} m_1 (r_1 \dot{\theta}_1)^2 + \tfrac{1}{2} m_2 \dot{r}_2{}^2 + \\ + \tfrac{1}{2} m_2 (r_2 \dot{\theta}_2)^2 + \{U_0 r_0 / (r_1 + r_2)\}, \qquad (420.3)$$

which indicates that the polar angles θ_1 and θ_2 are cyclic coordinates. We have the following relations between the coordinates.

$$\theta_1 - \theta_2 = \pi, \qquad (420.4)$$

$$r_1 + r_2 = r, \qquad (420.5)$$

$$m_1 r_1 - m_2 r_2 = 0. \qquad (420.6)$$

Equation (420.5) defines the separation r between the point masses, whereas (420.4) and (420.6) automatically follow because the origin of the coordinates falls on the center of mass.

† Taking two bodies of finite size, the external force applied to each body by the other through gravitational attraction acts on the center of mass. Hence, the discussion in this section may be applied to two bodies of finite size.

By solving (420.5) and (420.6) for the radial coordinates, we have

$$r_1 = m_2 r/(m_1 + m_2) \qquad (420.7)$$

and

$$r_2 = m_1 r/(m_1 + m_2), \qquad (420.8)$$

Inserting (420.4), (420.7), and (420.8) into that part of the Lagrangian that comes from the kinetic energy, and inserting (420.5) into the term from the potential energy, the Lagrangian may be reduced to the following expression

$$\mathcal{L} = \tfrac{1}{2} m \dot{r}^2 + \tfrac{1}{2} m(r\dot{\theta})^2 + \{U_0 r_0/r\}, \qquad (420.9)$$

in which m represents the *reduced mass*, e.g.,

$$m = m_1 m_2/(m_1 + m_2). \qquad (420.10)$$

We have dropped the subscript on the polar angle θ in (420.9). We are at liberty to let r point in the direction of either r_1 or r_2, and if we select r_1 then θ coincides with θ_1, but if we select r_2 for the direction of r then θ coincides with θ_2. Since the polar angle θ is a cyclic coordinate, it follows from Theorem I and the Lagrangian (420.9) that the angular momentum

$$f = \partial\mathcal{L}/\partial\dot{\theta} = mr^2\dot{\theta} = \text{const.}, \qquad (420.11)$$

is a constant of motion. Applying Theorem I to the Lagrangian once more gives the following equation of motion, which may be recognized as a statement of Newton's second law.

$$m(\ddot{r} - r\dot{\theta}^2) = -U_0 r_0/r^2. \qquad (420.12)$$

Some vectors which are related to this problem will now be introduced. A unit vector $\mathbf{1}_r$, which points in the direction of the radial separation r, is used in the definition of the radial vector,

$$\mathbf{r} = r\mathbf{1}_r, \qquad (420.13)$$

and the unit vector 1_θ is an axial vector normal to the orbital plane which is used to give a corresponding definition of the angular momentum vector,

$$\mathbf{f} = f \mathbf{1}_\theta . \qquad (420.14)$$

The cross product of the axial and radial unit vectors gives another unit vector

$$\mathbf{1}_n = \mathbf{1}_\theta \times \mathbf{1}_r , \qquad (420.15)$$

which lies in the orbital plane. It may be seen that the three unit vectors, $\mathbf{1}_r$, $\mathbf{1}_\theta$, and $\mathbf{1}_n$ are mutually orthogonal. The radial velocity and acceleration vectors may be written respectively

$$\dot{\mathbf{r}} = \dot{r} \mathbf{1}_r + r \dot{\theta} \mathbf{1}_n \qquad (420.16)$$

and

$$\ddot{\mathbf{r}} = (\ddot{r} - r\dot{\theta}^2) \mathbf{1}_r + (\ddot{\theta} r + 2\dot{\theta}\dot{r}) \mathbf{1}_n , \qquad (420.17)$$

where $\ddot{r}$ is the radial, $r\dot{\theta}^2$ the centripetal, $\ddot{\theta} r$ the angular, and $2\dot{\theta}\dot{r}$ the coriolis acceleration amplitude respectively. The coefficient $(\ddot{\theta} r + 2\dot{\theta}\dot{r})$ of $\mathbf{1}_n$ in (420.17) must vanish, since the gravitational force (420.12) can produce acceleration only in the direction of the unit vector $\mathbf{1}_r$. Hence, we may rewrite (420.12) as

$$m\ddot{\mathbf{r}} = - (U_0 r_0/r^2) \mathbf{1}_r . \qquad (420.18)$$

Furthermore, we may also rewrite the angular momentum vector in the form[†]

$$\mathbf{f} = m\mathbf{r} \times \dot{\mathbf{r}} = mr^2 \dot{\theta} \mathbf{1}_\theta . \qquad (420.19)$$

Now take the cross product $m\ddot{\mathbf{r}} \times \mathbf{f}$, using (420.18) and (420.19),

---

[†] It follows by simple construction that for each increment $d\mathbf{r}$, the radius vector $\mathbf{r}$ sweeps out an area dA equal to the magnitude of half the cross product $\mathbf{r} \times d\mathbf{r}$, e.g., $dA = |\mathbf{r} \times d\mathbf{r}|/2$. Hence, we have $\dot{A} = |\mathbf{r} \times \dot{\mathbf{r}}|/2$, which by (420.19) may be written $\dot{A} = |\mathbf{f}| (2m)^{-1}$. It follows from the conservation of angular momentum (420.11) that $\dot{A}$ is constant. Kepler's second law is the statement that $\dot{A}$ is constant.

e.g.,

$$m\ddot{\mathbf{r}} \times \mathbf{f} = mU_0 r_0 \dot{\theta} \mathbf{1}_n . \qquad (420.20)$$

It is necessary to take into account that the unit vectors $\mathbf{1}_r$ and $\mathbf{1}_n$ are in motion and that the time derivative of the unit vector $\mathbf{1}_r$ is given by the following cross product [see (201.6) and Fig. 2.1].

$$\dot{\mathbf{1}}_r = \dot{\theta}\mathbf{1}_\theta \times \mathbf{1}_r = \dot{\theta}\mathbf{1}_n . \qquad (420.21)$$

The next expression is obtained by inserting (420.21) into (420.20) and dividing through by $mU_0 r_0$.

$$\frac{\ddot{\mathbf{r}} \times \mathbf{f}}{U_0 r_0} = \dot{\mathbf{1}}_r . \qquad (420.22)$$

Next, Eq. (420.22) is integrated with respect to the time, and as the angular momentum $\mathbf{f}$ is constant, that integral may be written simply as

$$\frac{\dot{\mathbf{r}} \times \mathbf{f}}{U_0 r_0} = \mathbf{1}_r + b\mathbf{1}_a , \qquad (420.23)$$

in which b is a constant of integration and $\mathbf{1}_a$ is a unit vector lying in the orbital plane. Consider the following expression.

$$\mathbf{r} \cdot (\dot{\mathbf{r}} \times \mathbf{f}) = \mathbf{r} \cdot [\dot{\mathbf{r}} \times m(\mathbf{r} \times \dot{\mathbf{r}})] . \qquad (420.24)$$

As (420.24) is invariant under an exchange of the operations for taking the dot and cross products, it may also be written

$$\mathbf{r} \cdot (\dot{\mathbf{r}} \times \mathbf{f}) = m|\mathbf{r} \times \dot{\mathbf{r}}|^2 = f^2/m . \qquad (420.25)$$

It is easily seen from (420.25) that by taking the dot product of the radius vector $\mathbf{r}$ and both sides of (420.23), the latter reduces to

$$f^2/mU_0 r_0 = r(1 + b \cos \theta), \qquad (420.26)$$

in which θ is the angle between the unit vectors $\mathbf{1}_r$ and $\mathbf{1}_a$. As $\mathbf{1}_a$

has an arbitrary direction, we may use it as a reference for defining the polar angle θ. We have, from (420.26), the following well known formula for a conic section as the equation of the orbit,

$$r = \frac{f^2}{mU_0 r_0 (1 + b \cos \theta)} \qquad (420.27)$$

in which b gives the eccentricity. Equation (420.27) is a mathematical summary of Kepler's first law, which states that the orbits of the bodies in the solar system are conics, with the sun occupying one focus. The eccentricity is determined from (420.23) by taking the following steps. From (420.23) we have

$$b\mathbf{1}_a = \frac{\dot{\mathbf{r}} \times \mathbf{f}}{U_0 r_0} - \mathbf{1}_r . \qquad (420.28)$$

The square of the magnitude of (420.28) may be written

$$b^2 = 1 - \frac{2f^2}{mU_0 r_0 r} + \left| \frac{\dot{\mathbf{r}} \times \mathbf{f}}{U_0 r_0} \right|^2 . \qquad (420.29)$$

The relation (420.25) permits the writing of the second term on the right-hand side as given in (420.29). As $\dot{\mathbf{r}}$ is perpendicular to $\mathbf{f}$, it follows that $|\dot{\mathbf{r}} \times \mathbf{f}| = |\dot{\mathbf{r}}|\,|\mathbf{f}|$, and making this substitution in (420.29) makes it possible to write the following simple expressions for the eccentricity.

$$b^2 = 1 - \frac{2f^2}{mU_0 r_0 r} + \frac{|\dot{\mathbf{r}}|^2 f^2}{U_0^{\,2} r_0^{\,2}} , \qquad (420.30)$$

$$b^2 = 1 + \frac{2f^2}{mU_0^{\,2} r_0^{\,2}} \left(\frac{m}{2} |\dot{\mathbf{r}}|^2 - \frac{U_0 r_0}{r} \right). \qquad (420.31)$$

Corollary II applies to this system, and therefore it follows from Theorem II that the total energy is conserved and may be written

$$E = \dot{r} \frac{\partial \mathcal{L}}{\partial \dot{r}} + \dot{\theta} \frac{\partial \mathcal{L}}{\partial \dot{\theta}} - \mathcal{L}. \qquad (420.32)$$

By substituting (420.9) into (420.32) the expression for the total energy is obtained as

$$E = \tfrac{1}{2} m\dot{r}^2 + \tfrac{1}{2} mr^2\dot{\theta}^2 - \frac{U_0 r_0}{r}. \qquad (420.33)$$

By squaring the amplitude of the radial velocity vector given by (420.16) it may be seen that we may rewrite the total energy as

$$E = \tfrac{1}{2} m|\dot{\mathbf{r}}|^2 - \frac{U_0 r_0}{r}. \qquad (420.34)$$

The expression for the eccentricity is obtained by inserting (420.34) into (420.31) and taking the square root, which yields

$$b = \left(1 + \frac{2f^2 E}{mU_0{}^2 r_0{}^2}\right)^{\tfrac{1}{2}}. \qquad (420.35)$$

If the total energy is positive, the kinetic energy exceeds the binding energy $|U|$, and the orbit is that of a hyperbola ($b > 1$), but if the total energy is negative, the binding energy is greater than the kinetic energy, and the orbit is that of an ellipse ($b < 1$). If the total energy vanishes, the kinetic energy exactly equals the binding energy, and the orbit is a parabola ($b = 1$).

There are a number of different methods of obtaining the solution for the motion of two bodies under a central force, and the one just given is hardly the most concise, but it does provide the advantage of a simple physical interpretation for every mathematical step. Since this problem has become a classic, two additional solutions will be outlined. In the first of these, we establish the Lagrangian (420.9) and conservation of angular momentum (420.11) the same as before, but proceed from there with Theorem II instead of Theorem I, inserting (420.9) and (420.11) into (310.10) and invoking Corollary II to obtain the total energy expression

$$E = \frac{m\dot{r}^2}{2} + \frac{f^2}{2mr^2} - \frac{U_0 r_0}{r}. \tag{420.36}$$

By using the transformations

$$\frac{d}{dt} = \frac{f}{mr^2} \frac{d}{d\theta} \tag{420.37}$$

and

$$z = 1/r \tag{420.38}$$

in (420.36), we have

$$\left(\frac{dz}{d\theta}\right)^2 = -z^2 + \frac{2mU_0 r_0}{f^2} z + \frac{2mE}{f^2}. \tag{420.39}$$

The operation of completing the square yields

$$\left[\frac{d}{d\theta}\left(z - \frac{mU_0 r_0}{f^2}\right)\right]^2 + \left(z - \frac{mU_0 r_0}{f^2}\right)^2 = \left(\frac{mU_0 r_0}{f^2}\right)^2 + \frac{2mE}{f^2}, \tag{420.40}$$

which has the solution

$$z - \frac{mU_0 r_0}{f^2} = \left[\left(\frac{mU_0 r_0}{f^2}\right)^2 + \frac{2mE}{f^2}\right]^{\frac{1}{2}} \cos\theta. \tag{420.41}$$

Equation (420.41) reduces to the earlier solution (420.27) after z is replaced by $1/r$ and rearranging.

The other solution is the same as the first to (420.12). Then (420.11) is substituted into (420.12) to give

$$m\ddot{r} - \frac{f^2}{mr^3} + \frac{U_0 r_0}{r^2} = 0. \tag{420.42}$$

The transformation (420.37) is made on (420.42) to obtain the relation

$$\frac{d}{d\theta} \frac{1}{r^2} \frac{dr}{d\theta} - \frac{1}{r} + \frac{mU_0 r_0}{f^2} = 0, \tag{420.43}$$

and the transformation (420.38) is made on (420.43) to yield

$$\frac{d^2}{d\theta^2}\left(z - \frac{mU_0 r_0}{f^2}\right) + \left(z - \frac{mU_0 r_0}{f^2}\right) = 0, \quad (420.44)$$

which also has (420.41) as a solution.

Some of the classical properties of an ideal, lossless transformer are reviewed next, so that the magnetic flux defined here by (402.10) may be related to two line integrals which are commonly associated with transformer behavior, viz. the emf in the primary and secondary windings, and the mmf measured around a path linking both coils. First, consider one of the coils of the transformer taken by itself as illustrated schematically in

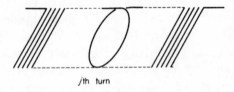

*j*th turn

Fig. 4.7. A coil with two sections drawn apart to expose the *j*th turn.

Fig. 4.7 with two sections of the coil separated so as to expose one single turn of the coil. Let that turn of the coil be designated as the *j*th turn, and for the moment we will consider the magnetic flux, its time derivative, and the emf associated with each turn of the coil separately and designate them respectively as g_j, $\dot{g}_j$, and V_j for the *j*th turn. It follows from electromagnetic theory that the emf for the *j*th turn may be written

$$V_j = -\oint_j \mathbf{E} \cdot \mathbf{dr} = \oint_j \dot{\mathbf{A}} \cdot \mathbf{dr} = \dot{g}_j. \quad (420.45)$$

Taking the line integrals around every turn from one end of the coil to the other gives for the total emf

$$V = \sum_{j=1}^{N} \dot{g}_j. \qquad (420.46)$$

Designating the mean flux per turn and its time derivative as g_0 and $\dot{g}_0$ respectively, we have

$$g_{\text{total}} = N g_0 \qquad (420.47)$$

for the total magnetic flux as given also by (402.10), and

$$V = N \dot{g}_0 \qquad (420.48)$$

for the total emf. The number of turns is taken into account only implicitly in the magnetic flux as given by (402.10) and in the emf as given by (402.18), whereas it enters explicitly in (420.47) and (420.48). Expressions (402.10) and (402.18) are preferable for general use, being more concise, but in this particular discussion, (420.47) and (420.48) are used in order to review the manner in which the number of turns enters into the properties of a transformer. A schematic diagram of a transformer is illustrated in Fig. 4.8. To consider the relationship between the emf of one winding as compared with the other, we take the case with the terminals of the coil on the right (Fig 4.8), which is disconnected so that there is no current flow in that winding ($\dot{q}_2 = 0$). To distinguish the properties related to the two windings, subscripts are added

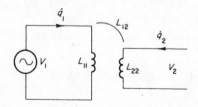

Fig. 4.8.   Schematic diagram of a transformer.

to the expression (420.48) and we write

$$V_1 = L_{11}\ddot{q}_1 = N_1\dot{g}_{10} \qquad (420.49)$$

and

$$V_2 = L_{12}\ddot{q}_1 = N_2\dot{g}_{20} \qquad (420.50)$$

for the emf of the coil on the left and the coil on the right respectively. On the average, each turn of coil 2 intercepts a certain fraction κ of the mean flux per turn generated by coil 1, and we may write

$$g_{20} = \kappa g_{10}, \quad 0 \leqslant \kappa < 1. \qquad (420.51)$$

By substituting (420.51) into the ratio of (420.49) to (420.50), the following relation between the turns ratio and the emf ratio is obtained.

$$\frac{V_1}{V_2} = \frac{L_{11}}{L_{12}} = \frac{N_1}{\kappa N_2}. \qquad (420.52)$$

By transferring the generator to the coil on the right (Fig. 4.8), and disconnecting the terminals of the coil on the left, the problem is left unchanged except for an interchange of subscripts 1 and 2, so that in this case the relation which corresponds to (420.52) may be written

$$\frac{V_2}{V_1} = \frac{L_{22}}{L_{12}} = \frac{N_2}{\kappa N_1}. \qquad (420.53)$$

The coupling coefficient κ may be obtained by taking the product of (420.52) and (420.53), yielding the relation

$$L_{12} = \kappa (L_{11}L_{22})^{\frac{1}{2}}. \qquad (420.54)$$

Relations (420.52), (420.53), and (420.54) indicate that the voltage ratio can be approximately equal to the turns ratio only for the limit of very tight coupling, with κ approaching unity as closely as possible.

Next we consider the mmf around the path indicated in Fig. 4.9 which shows a transformer with the secondary winding short circuited making V_2 vanish. As V_2 vanishes, we may write

$$- L_{12}\ddot{q}_1 + L_{22}\ddot{q}_2 = 0. \qquad (420.55)$$

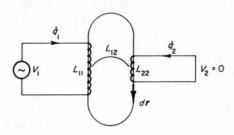

Fig. 4.9. Schematic diagram of a transformer with the secondary winding short circuited, showing the path around which the mmf is to be determined.

If we substitute (420.53) into (420.55), integrate with respect to the time, and recall (402.14), we have

$$- \kappa N_1\dot{q}_1 + N_2\dot{q}_2 = N_2 g_2/L_{22} = \text{const}. \qquad (420.56)$$

We take very general initial conditions, consisting of a voltage suddenly applied to the primary winding, with no initial current in either winding, e.g., $\dot{q}_1(0) = \dot{q}_2(0) = 0$, and $V_1(t) = 0$, with $t \leqslant 0$, and $V_1(t) \neq 0$, with $0 < t$. As we are concerned only with the magnetic flux g_2 produced by currents $\dot{q}_1$ and $\dot{q}_2$, then the flux g_2 is initially zero, but by (420.56) it must remain zero; thus we have the following relation between the turns ratio and the current ratio

$$\dot{q}_1/\dot{q}_2 = N_2/\kappa N_1. \qquad (420.57)$$

Equation (420.57) indicates that the ratio of the currents is approximately equal to the inverse turns ratio only for very tight coupling with κ approaching unity. The mmf is given by the well-known line integral

$$\text{mmf} = \oint \mathbf{H} \cdot \mathbf{dr} = \dot{q}_1 N_1 - \dot{q}_2 N_2 . \qquad (420.58)$$

The mmf may be expressed in terms of the ampere turns of the primary winding and the coupling coefficient by substituting (420.57) into (420.58) which yields the expression

$$\text{mmf} = (1 - \kappa)\dot{q}_1 N_1 . \qquad (420.59)$$

The circuit diagram of a resonant electromagnetic system is shown in Fig. 4.10. The secondary winding is short circuited and

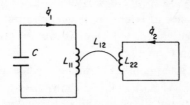

Fig. 4.10. Schematic diagram of a resonant electromagnetic system with a cyclic coordinate.

the effect of its presence on the oscillating primary circuit is the same as the effect of the interaction between the currents induced on the conducting wall and the coil of the oscillating circuit shown in Fig. 4.6. The Lagrangian for the system shown in Fig. 4.10 may be written

$$\mathcal{L} = \tfrac{1}{2} L_{11} \dot{q}_1{}^2 + \tfrac{1}{2} L_{22} \dot{q}_2{}^2 - L_{12} \dot{q}_1 \dot{q}_2 - (q_1{}^2/2C) . \qquad (420.60)$$

It may be seen from the Lagrangian (420.60) that q_2 is a cyclic coordinate. We apply Theorem I to the Lagrangian to obtain the following equations of motion.

$$L_{11}\ddot{q}_1 + (q_1/C) - L_{12}\ddot{q}_2 = 0 , \qquad (420.61)$$

$$- L_{12}\ddot{q}_1 + L_{22}\ddot{q}_2 = 0 . \qquad (420.62)$$

By substituting (420.62) into (420.61), the following equation of simple harmonic motion with one coordinate is obtained.

$$L_{11}(1 - \kappa^2)\ddot{q}_1 + (q_1/C) = 0. \qquad (420.63)$$

Hence, we see that the presence of the secondary winding merely reduces the inductance of the primary coil from L_{11} to $L_{11}(1 - \kappa^2)$. It is this result that explains the statement made earlier in connection with Fig. 4.4, that the conducting wall has no effect other than to reduce the inductances somewhat below the value they would otherwise have if the wall were absent.

If this were a more advanced treatment of analytical mechanics, we would include another axiom concerning the invariance of physical properties as functions of the coordinates in different frames of reference, in order to put some "teeth" into Axiom I and Postulate I. Also, in a more advanced presentation, the transformation of coordinates would not be restricted to the scleronomic but would include the rheonomic transformations. Then it could be shown, using some common parameter τ between all the coordinates including the time, that both the Lagrangian and the action are invariant.

Exercises

(4.1) This is a mechanical problem concerning the motion of two bodies with equal mass coupled by springs (see Fig. 4.11). The coordinates x_1 and x_2 respectively give the linear displace-

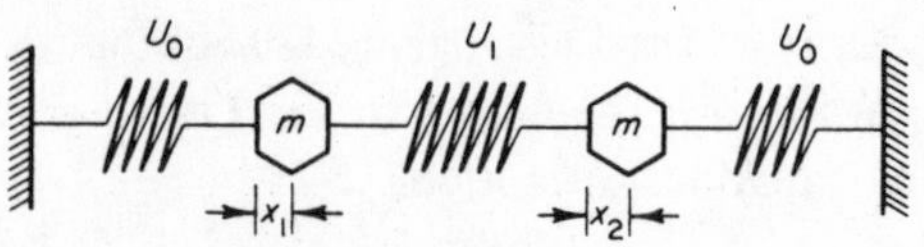

Fig. 4.11. Schematic diagram of two bodies with equal mass connected to two rigid supports by springs.

ment from the equilibrium position of each mass. Take positive values of the coordinates x_1 and x_2 to indicate displacement to the right of the equilibrium positions. The restoring force per unit displacement of the two springs anchored to the supports is given as a constant U_0, and for the center spring connected between the two masses, the corresponding constant is U_1. The force of gravity is to be neglected, as the behavior of the system is completely dominated by the restoring forces of the springs. Friction effects are also to be neglected in this problem. Show that the Lagrangian may be written

$$\mathscr{L} = \tfrac{1}{2} m \dot{x}_1{}^2 + \tfrac{1}{2} m \dot{x}_2{}^2 + \tfrac{1}{2} U_1 (x_2 - x_1)^2 + \tfrac{1}{2} U_0 (x_1{}^2 + x_2{}^2),$$

and the equations of motion are

$$\begin{pmatrix} [md^2/dt^2 + (U_0 + U_1)] & -U_1 \\ -U_1 & [md^2/dt^2 + (U_0 + U_1)] \end{pmatrix}$$
$$\begin{pmatrix} x_1 \\ x_2 \end{pmatrix} = \begin{pmatrix} 0 \\ 0 \end{pmatrix},$$

and that the natural frequencies are given by $(U_0/m)^{\frac{1}{2}}$ and $(\{U_0 + 2U_1\}/m)^{\frac{1}{2}}$.

(4.2) Consider the compound pendulum illustrated in Fig. 4.12. The body with mass m_1 is connected to a rod of constant length r_1 with negligible weight which is, in turn, connected to

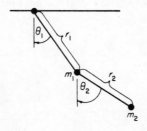

Fig. 4.12. Compound pendulum.

the support by a frictionless pivot permitting the mass m_1 to rotate in a plane making an angle θ_1 with the vertical. The body, mass m_2, is connected to a weightless rod with constant length r_2, which is connected to the body with mass m_1 by a frictionless pivot, permitting the mass m_2 to rotate in the same plane of motion as mass m_1 and make an angle θ_2 with the vertical. The only force acting on the bodies is that of gravitational attraction contributing a constant acceleration γ. Show that the Lagrangian of the system is given by

$$\mathcal{L} = \tfrac{1}{2}(m_1 + m_2)(r_1\dot\theta_1)^2$$
$$+ \tfrac{1}{2} m_2 \left[(r_2\dot\theta_2)^2 + 2r_1r_2\dot\theta_1\dot\theta_2 \cos(\theta_2 - \theta_1)\right]$$
$$- \gamma \left[(m_1 + m_2)r_1(1 - \cos\theta_1) + m_2r_2(1 - \cos\theta_2)\right].$$

Make an approximation of the Lagrangian suitable for motion restricted to small amplitudes, giving as the equations of motion

$$(m_1 + m_2)\, r_1^2 \ddot\theta_1 + \gamma(m_1 + m_2)\, r_1\theta_1 + m_2r_1r_2\ddot\theta_2 = 0,$$

and

$$m_2r_1r_2\ddot\theta_1 + m_2r_2^2\ddot\theta_2 + \gamma m_2 r_2 \theta_2 = 0.$$

Show that the equations of motion yield the following natural frequencies of the system.

$$\frac{\gamma}{2}\left(\frac{r_1 + r_2}{r_1 r_2}\right)\left(\frac{m_1 + m_2}{m_1}\right)\left\{1 \pm \left[1 - \frac{4m_1 r_1 r_2}{(m_1 + m_2)(r_1 + r_2)^2}\right]^{\frac{1}{2}}\right\}.$$

(**4.3**) Consider two loosely coupled identical oscillators as illustrated in Fig. 4.13. Show that the equations of motion may

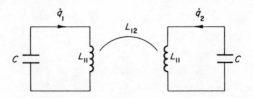

Fig. 4.13. Schematic diagram of two loosely coupled identical oscillators.

be written

$$\begin{bmatrix} \left(L_{11}\dfrac{d^2}{dt^2} + \dfrac{1}{C}\right) & -L_{12}\dfrac{d^2}{dt^2} \\[2ex] -L_{12}\dfrac{d^2}{dt^2} & \left(L_{11}\dfrac{d^2}{dt^2} + \dfrac{1}{C}\right) \end{bmatrix} \begin{bmatrix} q_1 \\[2ex] q_2 \end{bmatrix} = \begin{bmatrix} 0 \\[2ex] 0 \end{bmatrix}.$$

Show that, if the coupling coefficient κ is small compared with unity ($\kappa = L_{12}/L_{11} \ll 1$), the resonant frequencies are given by the expression

$$[1 \pm \kappa/2]/(L_{11}C)^{\frac{1}{2}},$$

and that either the current $\dot{q}_1$ or $\dot{q}_2$ may be expressed in the form

$$\tfrac{1}{2}\left[\cos(1 - \tfrac{1}{2}\kappa)\,t/(L_{11}C)^{\frac{1}{2}} - \cos(1 + \tfrac{1}{2}\kappa)\,t/(L_{11}C)^{\frac{1}{2}}\right],$$

or

$$(\sin \tfrac{1}{2}\kappa\ t/(L_{11}C)^{\frac{1}{2}}) \sin t/(L_{11}C)^{\frac{1}{2}}.$$

(4.4) A spheroid is mounted on gimbals so that it may rotate about its axis of symmetry and an axis through its equatorial plane. The axes of rotation are inclined at an angle θ with respect to two rectangular coordinates in which the components of angular rotation are specified as ω_1 and ω_2. Consider the angular momentum of the spheroid

$$\begin{pmatrix} f_1 \\ f_2 \end{pmatrix} = \begin{pmatrix} I_{11} & I_{12} \\ I_{12} & I_{22} \end{pmatrix} \begin{pmatrix} \omega_1 \\ \omega_2 \end{pmatrix}.$$

We may write tentatively $\begin{pmatrix} f_1 \\ f_2 \end{pmatrix} = I\begin{pmatrix} \omega_1 \\ \omega_2 \end{pmatrix}$, and when the components ω_1 and ω_2 are "proper values" making $\begin{pmatrix} \omega_1 \\ \omega_2 \end{pmatrix}$ coincide with the axis of symmetry, then $I = I_1$, the moment of inertia about the axis of symmetry. Similarly, when ω_1 and ω_2 are "proper values" making $\begin{pmatrix} \omega_1 \\ \omega_2 \end{pmatrix}$ coincide with the axis of rotation in the equatorial plane, then $I = I_2$, the moment of inertia about the axis in the equatorial plane. In those cases $\begin{pmatrix} f_1 \\ f_2 \end{pmatrix} = I\begin{pmatrix} \omega_1 \\ \omega_2 \end{pmatrix}$, but otherwise

$\binom{f_1}{f_2} \neq I\binom{\omega_1}{\omega_2}$. Hence, we may write a "proper value" matrix equation

$$\begin{pmatrix} I_{11} & I_{12} \\ I_{12} & I_{22} \end{pmatrix} \begin{pmatrix} \omega_1 \\ \omega_2 \end{pmatrix} = I \begin{pmatrix} \omega_1 \\ \omega_2 \end{pmatrix},$$

or

$$\begin{pmatrix} (I_{11} - I) & I_{12} \\ I_{12} & (I_{22} - I) \end{pmatrix} \begin{pmatrix} \omega_1 \\ \omega_2 \end{pmatrix} = \begin{pmatrix} 0 \\ 0 \end{pmatrix}.$$

The solution of the quadratic equation given by the secular determinant gives the moments of inertia about the principal axes. Show that with $I_{11} = (3I_1 + I_2)/4$, $I_{22} = (I_1 + 3I_2)/4$, and $I_{12} = \sqrt{3}(I_1 - I_2)/4$, the principal moments of inertia are I_1 and I_2. Also show that the principal axes are inclined at an angle $\theta = \pi/6$ with the coordinates.

(4.5) Consider the orbital period of the radius vector **r** in the example of two bodies bound by a central force (see Section 4.2). Prove the following theorem, which is a statement of Kepler's third law. *The squares of the periods of the planets are proportional to the cubes of their orbital major axes.* Hint: The period T times the areal velocity $\dot{A} = |\mathbf{f}|(2m)^{-1}$ equals the area of an ellipse, i.e., π times the product of the semimajor and semiminor axes, and $\dot{A}$ is constant by Kepler's second law.

CHAPTER 4 BIBLIOGRAPHY

Joos, G. (1934). "Theoretical Physics." Hafner, New York.

Marion, J. B. (1965). "Classical Dynamics of Particles and Systems." Academic Press, New York. A more complete treatment of the problem of two bodies moving under a central force than that given here may be found in this reference. The behavior of nonlinear oscillators, which has not been discussed here, has been treated by Marion at an intermediate level in clear detail.

CHAPTER 5

Nonconservative
Linear Systems

Consider the undamped simple harmonic oscillator completely enclosed by a conducting wall (Fig. 4.6). If part of the wall were removed, as illustrated in Fig. 5.1, then energy could

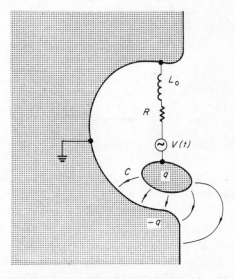

Fig. 5.1. A simple harmonic oscillator with damping.

radiate away from the system even if it were composed entirely of ideal conductors. Thus, by merely taking the lid off, we have converted a conservative into a nonconservative system. A similar comparison might be made between the enclosed conservative system with two degrees of freedom (Fig. 4.4) and the nonconservative system with two degrees of freedom shown in

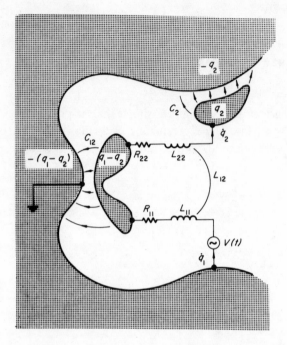

Fig. 5.2. Schematic representation of an electrical network with two independent variables.

Fig. 5.2. If the enclosure had been left intact in Fig. 4.6, but the ideal conductors had been replaced by ordinary conductors, then the energy of the system could also escape through the Joule heat loss to the conducting bodies. Continuing with the same system, but taking more of its physical properties into account by including the crystal lattice vibrations of the conductors, it may be seen that the energy has not left the system, but has spread throughout it by the laws of statistical mechanics. If the system is examined with sufficient resolution, one finds that its parts are oscillating with a mean square amplitude depending on the total energy shared by the system, or in other words, by its temperature.

We here construct the boundaries around each physical system in such a way as to ignore the thermal vibrations of its parts, so as to account for energy losses without examining the detailed mechanisms of dissipation.

An abridged version of the following discussion has appeared elsewhere (Gossick, 1967).

5.0. A Lagrangian Formulation for Nonconservative Linear Systems

In trying to apply a variational treatment to nonconservative physical systems, one immediately finds a dilemma. There are firmly ingrained traditions established through the treatment of conservative systems by Hamilton's principle, and the rigid adherence to all these traditions seems incompatible with the treatment of nonconservative systems.

First consider the *action integral*. If one attempts to follow tradition by calling the corresponding integral by that name, one then violates tradition in another sense as the integral comes out with the dimensions of energy. The ultimate solution here is to adopt an integral which bears neither the name nor the dimensions of action, and to call it the *complex power*.[†]

If one makes use of Fourier methods another problem is encountered. The interval of time under consideration in the treatment of a conservative system by Hamilton's principle is arbitrarily chosen. The treatment by Fourier series would seem adequate to describe the behavior of a system within an arbitrarily designated interval of time, although that particular solution would not in general describe the behavior outside that prescribed interval. However, one should be able to develop appropriate Fourier series solutions for the behavior of the

[†] The complex power related to the force J and the velocity $\dot{y}$ is defined by the relation

$$\mathscr{P}^* = (t_2 - t_1)^{-1} \int_{t_1}^{t_2} \tfrac{1}{2} J^* \dot{y}\, dt \,,$$

over the interval t_1 to t_2.

system over all other time intervals. The versatility of Fourier series would appear to make it possible in this special sense to comply with tradition, but it would frequently lead to unnecessarily complicated solutions. The final decision here is to relax the condition on the interval over which the *complex power* is integrated, so that it may be selected to suit the problem under consideration.

Consider the task of formulating the Lagrangian function of a nonconservative linear system. It is assumed that the Lagrangian function does not depend explicitly on the time. It is also assumed that the coordinates of the system y_j, $j = 1, 2, 3, \ldots n$ are independent. However, in case some of the coordinates are interrelated through holonomic or nonholonomic conditions, the method of Lagrangian multipliers may be applied to the treatment for nonconservative systems given here, the same as for conservative systems. We assume that the Lagrangian may be split into two parts, one for the conservative and the other for the dissipative properties of the system, as stipulated by the following postulate, in which it may be seen that the nonconservative Lagrangian term has the dimensions of power, while the conservative Lagrangian term has the dimensions of energy.

When we took Hamilton's principle as the starting point for the treatment of conservative systems, we introduced Postulate II to specify the form of the Lagrangian function. Here Postulate IIa serves as the extension of that postulate for nonconservative systems.

Postulate IIa: That part of the Lagrangian which accounts for energy dissipated by the system is summarized by the two functions F and Π, e.g.,

$$\mathscr{L}'' = F + \Pi, \tag{500.1}$$

in which[†]

$$F = \tfrac{1}{2} \dot{y}_i R_{ij} \dot{y}_j \tag{500.2}$$

[†] The summation convention for repeated subscripts is used throughout.

is Rayleigh's dissipation function ($\frac{1}{2}$ the power consumed by relaxation processes) and

$$\Pi = \tfrac{1}{2} \ddot{y}_i P_{ij} \ddot{y}_j \qquad (500.3)$$

is one half the power lost by radiation. The matrix elements R_{ij} and P_{ij} are real constants and symmetric. The function $\mathscr{L}'$ accounts for energy stored in the system and is the same as the Lagrangian for conservative systems, e.g.,

$$\mathscr{L}' = T - U, \qquad (500.4)$$

with T the kinetic energy and U the potential energy.

Given Postulate IIa, one finds that any nonconservative linear system has the following equations of motion (Gossick, 1967)

$$\left\{ \frac{\partial \mathscr{L}''}{\partial \dot{y}_j} - \frac{d}{dt} \frac{\partial \mathscr{L}''}{\partial \ddot{y}_j} \right\} - \left\{ \frac{\partial \mathscr{L}'}{\partial y_j} - \frac{d}{dt} \frac{\partial \mathscr{L}'}{\partial \dot{y}_j} \right\} = J_j, \qquad (500.5)$$

with J_j a component of external force applied along the coordinate y_j. Neglecting the radiation contribution Π, (500.5) reduces to Rayleigh's *ad hoc* statement (Rayleigh, 1873, 1877).

If we take U as the quadratic function of the coordinates $\frac{1}{2} y_s U_{sj} y_j$ and T as the sum of a quadratic term $\frac{1}{2} \dot{y}_s M_{sj} \dot{y}_j$ and a gyroscopic term $\frac{1}{2} \dot{y}_s G_{sj} y_j$, then (500.5) reduces to the linear equations of motion

$$- P_{js}\dddot{y}_s + M_{js}\ddot{y}_s + B_{js}\dot{y}_s + U_{js}y_s = J_j, \qquad (500.6)$$

with $B_{js} = R_{js} + G_{js}$. The matrix elements M_{js}, G_{js}, and U_{js} are real constants, and M_{js} and U_{js} are symmetrical while G_{js} is antisymmetrical. Let us test (500.6) on two simple examples.

Consider the dynamic behavior of the valence electrons in a metal as treated classically by the model of Drude. If we were able to write the equations of motion for all the electrons and ionic cores in the metal, there would be an appropriate scleronomic translation of coordinates (400.14) that would diagonalize the secular matrix and leave only independent equations of motion. We do not know how to make the transformation which relates a coordinate x with the actual displacement y in the metal, so we write the equation of motion for a single particle (500.6) and assume it to be an independent equation that we would obtain if we knew how to make the proper transformation. This procedure has been followed at various levels of sophistication since the turn of the century, and we are operating here on the most elementary level.

The equation of motion of the form (500.6) is used in the Drude model and is customarily said to represent the typical valence electron, although what it should represent is a spectral component of a valence electron. The coordinate x is regarded as the effective displacement of the typical electron with charge $-q$ and mass m. The mass m is not necessarily the true mass, but rather an effective mass which varies somewhat from metal to metal.[†] The term $M_{js}\ddot{y}_s$ refers in this case to the product of the mass and acceleration, given here by $m\ddot{x}$, while all the other terms represent forces. If the electron is in a tiny particle of metal (Gossick, 1963), then it is subject to an elastic restoring force proportional to the displacement, and the term $U_{js}y_s$ may be written $m\omega_0^2 x$, but this term vanishes if the bulk metal is under consideration. There are relaxation processes in which valence electrons give up energy to the crystal lattice of the metal, or to impurities lodged in the metal, and these occur at a rate which is proportional to the velocity $\dot{x}$ which effect is summarized in the term $R_{js}\dot{y}_s$, and in this example is written $(m/\tau)\dot{x}$ with τ a relaxation time. The electron is also subject to a *radiation reaction force*[††] $(q^2/6\pi\varepsilon_0 c^3)\dddot{x}$ in which c is the velocity of light, and this

[†] There is a current theoretical model in which even the electronic charge is replaced by an effective charge.

[††] The *radiation reaction force* is explained in standard texts on electromagnetic theory, e.g., see A. Sommerfeld, "Electrodynamics," Sect. 36, Academic Press, New York (1952). A common term in the literature, "radiation damping," refers to damping loss produced by the radiation reaction force.

effect is taken into account in the first term on the left-hand side
of (500.6). If there is an oscillating applied electric field, then
there is an external force $-qE_0e^{i\omega t}$ to represent J_j on the right-
hand side in (500.6). Hence, the typical electron has the following
equation of motion.

$$-(q^2/6\pi\varepsilon_0c^3)\dddot{x} + m\ddot{x} + (m/\tau)\dot{x} + m\omega_0{}^2x = -qE_0e^{i\omega t}.$$
$$(500.7)$$

We ignore that part of the solution of (500.7) which comes from
the homogeneous equation, as the behavior of the system is
completely summarized in the steady state solution anyway. By
solving (500.7) for the steady state velocity, we have

$$\dot{x} = -\frac{q\tau E_0e^{i\omega t}}{m}\left[1 + \frac{q^2\tau\omega^2}{6\pi\varepsilon_0mc^3} + i\omega_0\tau\left(\frac{\omega}{\omega_0} - \frac{\omega_0}{\omega}\right)\right]^{-1}. \quad (500.8)$$

The *complex power* for the example (500.8) may be written

$$\frac{qE^*\dot{x}}{2} = \frac{q^2\tau E_0{}^2}{2m}\left[1 + \frac{q^2\tau\omega^2}{6\pi\varepsilon_0mc^3} + i\omega_0\tau\left(\frac{\omega}{\omega_0} - \frac{\omega_0}{\omega}\right)\right]^{-1}, \quad (500.9)$$

the real part of which is the familiar absorption curve, and the
imaginary part the dispersion curve, when plotted against the
frequency ω. The radiation reaction force contributes only the
term $q^2\tau\omega^2/6\pi\varepsilon_0mc^3$ in (500.9), and, except for a small variation
in the effective mass m, the magnitude of that term varies only
through the relaxation time τ and the frequency ω. Over the
common temperature range, silver has the greatest relaxation
time, 40.9×10^{-15} sec $0°C$, and therefore should exhibit the
greatest effect. However, one finds that the effect is negligible
even at ultraviolet frequencies. It commences to be significant
in the region of soft X rays where the energy is of the order of,
or exceeding, 10^3 eV.

Consider the behavior of an electromagnetic circuit of the kind
illustrated in Figure 5.1, viz. the series resonant circuit. In this

case, the role of the independent coordinate y in (500.6) is played by the charge q on the capacitance C, while the potential coefficient U_{js} is given by $1/C$. The inertial coefficient M_{js} is given by the inductance L_0, the coefficient R_{js} refers to the resistance R, while the coefficient P_{js}, given here by P, applies to the electric dipole radiation loss. It is assumed throughout that the electromagnetic energy associated with any circuit has a wavelength which is very large compared with the dimensions of the individual circuit elements. The external force J_j on the right-hand side of (500.6) is represented here by the oscillating emf, $V(t) = V_0 e^{i\omega t}$. Therefore, the series resonant circuit has the equation of motion

$$-P\ddot{q} + L_0\ddot{q} + R\dot{q} + (q/C) = V_0 e^{i\omega t}. \qquad (500.10)$$

The following solution of (500.10) gives the steady state current,

$$\dot{q} = \frac{V_0 e^{i\omega t}}{R + \omega^2 P + i\left(\dfrac{L_0}{C}\right)^{\frac{1}{2}}\left(\dfrac{\omega}{\omega_0} - \dfrac{\omega_0}{\omega}\right)}, \qquad (500.11)$$

in which $\omega_0 = 1/(L_0 C)^{\frac{1}{2}}$. Taking the complex power, we have

$$\frac{V^*\dot{q}}{2} = \frac{V_0^2}{2}\left[R + \omega^2 P + i\left(\frac{L_0}{C}\right)^{\frac{1}{2}}\left(\frac{\omega}{\omega_0} - \frac{\omega_0}{\omega}\right)\right]^{-1}. \qquad (500.12)$$

Unless the circuit has been designed deliberately to make R as small as possible, the resistive term $\omega^2 P$ is negligible. In those cases where $\omega^2 P$ is not entirely negligible, its effect can be noticed only in the narrow frequency range near resonance $\omega \sim \omega_0$, so that, in those cases, where $\omega^2 P$ does enter, it ordinarily may be replaced by $\omega_0^2 P$. Hence, the energy losses by both relaxation processes and radiation are ordinarily combined, letting R denote the sum $R + \omega_0^2 P$. The term $\omega_0^2 P$ is referred to in the literature as the "radiation resistance."

For reasons illustrated by the two examples just given, we usually ignore the first term on the left-hand side of (500.6), and assume that power losses are adequately treated by the abridged expression

$$M_{js}\ddot{y}_s + R_{js}\dot{y}_s + U_{js}y_s = J_j. \qquad (500.13)$$

In the next section we commence with (500.6) as a lemma, and derive a result which suitably defines both the Lagrangian function (consistent with Postulate IIa) and the *complex power* of the system. Also, it is shown that when no external forces are applied to the system, Eq. (500.5) may be made to yield a vanishing variation of the *complex power*.

5.0.1. The Complex Power

…We may thus without any real loss of generality confine ourselves to periodic, and therefore by Fourier's theorem to harmonic forces…
Lord Rayleigh

Consider the generality of expressing functions of time by Fourier series. All periodic functions are automatically included. As we are at liberty to make the fundamental period as long as we please, we may have it extend over the entire time interval of interest, viz., the interval $t_2 - t_1$, over which the complex power is averaged. Certainly almost any function of time that could describe the behavior of a physical system could be described in this way, in terms of its spectral composition with $t_2 - t_1$ serving as the fundamental period. For example, with a simple steady state periodic solution, the fundamental period would be $t_2 - t_1$. But, with a transient solution superimposed on the periodic solution, the interval $t_2 - t_1$ must be made a sufficiently large multiple of the period of the applied force $J_j(t)$ so that the natural modes of the system have time to damp out and become negligible within the interval $t_2 - t_1$. Otherwise, any transient problem of the kind that may be handled by the

method of Fourier integrals may be treated by taking the interval $t_2 - t_1$ long enough to make the Fourier series adequately
approximate the Fourier integral (see Chapter 2, Section 2.1.0).
With these remarks in mind, we treat the external force and the
coordinates and their time derivatives as Fourier series, with
frequencies $\omega_k = 2\pi k/(t_2 - t_1)$, $k = 0, \pm 1, \pm 2, \pm 3, \dots$. We take
the coordinates $y_s(t)$ and their time derivatives to be single-
valued and periodic in the sense $y_s(t) = y_s(t + n\tau_0)$, with $n = \pm 1$,
$\pm 2, \pm 3, \dots$ and $\tau_0 = t_2 - t_1$. Thus, we may write (500.6) as[†]

$$\sum_k \left[- i\omega_k P_{js} \ddot{y}_s(k) + i\omega_k M_{js} \dot{y}_s(k) + B_{js} \dot{y}_s(k) \right.$$
$$\left. + U_{js} y_s(k) \right] e^{i\omega_k t} = J_j(t). \tag{501.1}$$

Now we write the conjugate transpose of (501.1) as

$$\sum_k \left[i\omega_k \ddot{y}_s(k)^* P_{sj} - i\omega_k \dot{y}_s(k)^* M_{sj} + \dot{y}_s(k)^* R_{sj} \right.$$
$$\left. - \dot{y}_s(k)^* G_{sj} + y_s(k)^* U_{sj} \right] e^{-i\omega_k t} = J_j(t)^*. \tag{501.2}$$

The next step is to multiply through by $\dot{y}_j/2$ and average over
the fundamental period.

$$\tfrac{1}{2} \sum_k \left[\dot{y}_s(k)^* R_{sj} \dot{y}_j(k) + \ddot{y}_s(k)^* P_{sj} \ddot{y}_j(k) - \dot{y}_s(k)^* G_{sj} \dot{y}_j(k) \right.$$
$$\left. - i\omega_k \{ \dot{y}_s(k)^* M_{sj} \dot{y}_j(k) - y_s(k)^* U_{sj} y_j(k) \} \right]$$
$$= (t_2 - t_1)^{-1} \sum_j \int_{t_1}^{t_2} \tfrac{1}{2} J_j^* \dot{y}_j \, dt. \tag{501.3}$$

Let us denote the spectral amplitude, phase and phase difference

---

[†] We write the coordinates, their time derivatives and forces as the
periodic complex functions,

$$y_j(t) = \sum_k y_{jk}(t) = \sum_k y_j(k) \, e^{i\omega_k t}, \qquad \dot{y}_j(t) = \sum_k \dot{y}_{jk}(t) = \sum_k \dot{y}_j(k) \, e^{i\omega_k t},$$
$$\ddot{y}_j(t) = \sum_k \ddot{y}_{jk}(t) = \sum_k \ddot{y}(k) \, e^{i\omega_k t}, \qquad J_j(t) = \sum_k J(k) \, e^{i\omega_k t}$$

by the expressions

$$\dot{y}_s(k) = |\dot{y}_s(k)| e^{i\gamma_s(k)},\qquad(501.4)$$

and

$$\gamma_{js}(k) = \gamma_j(k) - \gamma_s(k).\qquad(501.5)$$

Because of the symmetry of P_{js}, M_{js}, R_{js}, and U_{js}, and the anti-symmetry of G_{js}, the terms in $\sin \gamma_{js}(k)$ vanish in the former group and the terms in $\cos \gamma_{js}(k)$ vanish in the latter in summing over the subscripts j and s. We may therefore write (501.3) as follows.

$$\frac{1}{2}\sum_k \big[\,|\dot{y}_s(k)| R_{sj} |\dot{y}_j(k)| + |\ddot{y}_s(k)| P_{sj} |\ddot{y}_j(k)|$$
$$- i\omega_k \{|\dot{y}_s(k)| M_{sj} |\dot{y}_j(k)|$$
$$- |y_s(k)| U_{sj} |y_j(k)|\}\big] \cos \gamma_{js}(k)$$
$$- \frac{1}{2}\sum_k i\omega_k |\dot{y}_s(k)| G_{sj} |y_j(k)| \sin \gamma_{js}(k)$$
$$= (t_2 - t_1)^{-1} \sum_j \int_{t_1}^{t_2} \tfrac{1}{2} J_j^* \dot{y}_j \, dt.\qquad(501.6)$$

By using the relations cited in Chapter 2, Section 2.1.1 as (211.6) and (211.7), we may rewrite (501.6) as

$$2\sum_k \{F_k + \overline{\Pi}_k - i\omega_k[\overline{T}_k - \overline{U}_k]\}$$
$$= (t_2 - t_1)^{-1} \sum_j \int_{t_1}^{t_2} \tfrac{1}{2} J_j^* \dot{y}_j \, dt,\qquad(501.7)$$

in which the average values of the real functions F, Π, T, and U for each component of the spectrum are given by $\overline{F}_k$, $\overline{\Pi}_k$, $\overline{T}_k$, and $\overline{U}_k$ respectively. Hence, we may write (501.7) in the form

$$2(t_2 - t_1)^{-1} \sum_k \int_{t_1}^{t_2} \{F_k + \Pi_k - i\omega_k[T_k - U_k]\} \, dt$$
$$= (t_2 - t_1)^{-1} \sum_j \int_{t_1}^{t_2} \tfrac{1}{2} J_j^* \dot{y}_j \, dt,\qquad(501.8)$$

which may be recognized as the *complex power* of the system. The real part of the expression on the right-hand side of (501.8) gives the power irreversibly supplied to the system, and this equals the real term on the left-hand side which is the power dissipated by the system. The factor 2 on the left-hand side enters because F and Π were originally specified as one half the rates of energy dissipation. The *reactive power* has been a standard term used for many years by electrical engineers to denote the imaginary part of the *complex power* (501.8), which refers to the rate that the energy alternately transfers from potential energy to kinetic energy and back and forth with any excess of one over the other being exchanged with the external forces. ·The factor 2 enters in the imaginary part of (501.8) because the potential and kinetic energies vary with frequency components $2\omega_k$ whereas the coordinates themselves have frequency components ω_k.

By referring to Postulate IIa we may write (501.8) as

$$2(t_2 - t_1)^{-1} \sum_k \int_{t_1}^{t_2} \left[\mathscr{L}_k'' - i\omega_k \mathscr{L}_k' \right] dt$$
$$= (t_2 - t_1)^{-1} \sum_j \int_{t_1}^{t_2} \tfrac{1}{2} J_j^* \dot{y}_j \, dt, \qquad (501.9)$$

in which the component $\mathscr{L}_k''$ is obtained by writing $\mathscr{L}''$ using just the components of $\dot{y}_j$ and $\ddot{y}_j$ for the frequency ω_k, and the component $\mathscr{L}_k'$ is obtained by writing $\mathscr{L}'$ using just the components of y_j and $\dot{y}_j$ for the frequency ω_k.[†] Now if we take the

---

[†] To decompose the Lagrangian $\mathscr{L}$ into its components $\mathscr{L}_k$, one may refer to Chapter 2, Section 2.1.1, apply (211.4) and (211.7) to (501.6) and (501.9), and write,

$$\mathscr{L}'' = \underbrace{[\text{Re } \dot{y}_{sk}(t)] \tfrac{1}{2} R_{sj} [\text{Re } \dot{y}_{jk}(t)]}_{F_k} + \underbrace{[\text{Re } \ddot{y}_{sk}(t)] \tfrac{1}{2} P_{sj} [\text{Re } \ddot{y}_{jk}(t)]}_{\Pi_k}$$

$$\mathscr{L}'_k = \underbrace{[\text{Re } \dot{y}_{sk}(t)] \tfrac{1}{2} M_{sj} [\text{Re } \dot{y}_{jk}(t)] + [\text{Re } \dot{y}_{sk}(t)] \tfrac{1}{2} G_{sj} [\text{Re } y_{jk}(t)]}_{T_k}$$

$$- \underbrace{[\text{Re } y_{sk}(t)] \tfrac{1}{2} U_{sj} [\text{Re } y_{jk}(t)]}_{U_k}.$$

following expression

$$\mathscr{L} = \sum_k \left[\mathscr{L}_k'' - i\omega_k \mathscr{L}_k' \right], \quad k = 0, \pm 1, \pm 2, \ldots \quad (501.10)$$

as the Lagrangian of the system, and write the *complex power* by the following relation

$$\mathscr{P}^* = 2(t_2 - t_1)^{-1} \int_{t_1}^{t_2} \mathscr{L} \, dt, \quad (501.11)$$

then (501.8) may be written in the following concise form.

$$\mathscr{P}^* = 2(t_2 - t_1)^{-1} \int_{t_1}^{t_2} \mathscr{L} \, dt = (t_2 - t_1)^{-1} \sum_j \int_{t_1}^{t_2} \tfrac{1}{2} J_j^* \dot{y}_j \, dt. \quad (501.12)$$

By inspecting (501.8) and (501.12) it may be seen that minimum real *complex power* gives minimum energy dissipation while minimum imaginary *complex power* gives minimum difference between kinetic and potential energy.

It is obvious that when the functions T, U, F, and Π are quadratic forms, as in (402.21), (500.2) and (500.3), then each of them is invariant, and therefore the Lagrangian (501.10) is also invariant, under a scleronomic transformation of coordinates.

If there are no external forces on the system, it follows immediately from (501.12) that the *complex power* is stationary. Even so, we proceed to show in the next section that when all the external forces J_j vanish, then the equations of motion (500.5) lead to a vanishing variation of the *complex power*.

Now we consider only forces which may be expressed as functions of the coordinates of the system, i.e., the forces which may be derived from the potential function U. Thus, we may write (500.5) as the following sum of spectral components.

$$\sum_k \left[\left(\frac{\partial \mathscr{L}_k''}{\partial \dot{y}_j} - \frac{d}{dt} \frac{\partial \mathscr{L}_k''}{\partial \ddot{y}_j} \right) - \left(\frac{\partial \mathscr{L}_k'}{\partial y_j} - \frac{d}{dt} \frac{\partial \mathscr{L}_k'}{\partial \dot{y}_j} \right) \right] = 0. \quad (501.13)$$

We now permit (501.13) to represent a complex function and take its conjugate transpose.

$$\sum_k \left[\left(\frac{\partial \mathscr{L}_k''}{\partial \dot{y}_j} - \frac{d}{dt} \frac{\partial \mathscr{L}_k''}{\partial \ddot{y}_j} \right)^* - \left(\frac{\partial \mathscr{L}_k'}{\partial y_j} - \frac{d}{dt} \frac{\partial \mathscr{L}_k'}{\partial \dot{y}_j} \right)^* \right] = 0.$$

(501.14)

Consider the following variations in the coordinates

$$\delta y_j(t) = \varphi_j(t) = \sum_k \varphi_{jk}(t),$$ (501.15)

with

$$\varphi_{jk}(t) = -i \varphi_{jk0} \exp\left[i(\omega_k t - \theta_k) \right],$$ (501.16)

$$\operatorname{Re} \varphi_{jk}(t) = \varphi_{jk0} \sin(\omega_k t - \theta_k),$$ (501.17)

and with the amplitudes φ_{jk0} real and the phase shifts given by the relation

$$\theta_k = \omega_k t_1$$ (501.18)

which makes both $\operatorname{Re} \varphi_j(t_1)$ and $\operatorname{Re} \varphi_j(t_2)$ vanish as required in the general applications of Hamilton's principle. We now multiply (501.14) through by $\dot{\varphi}_j$ and integrate over the fundamental period. Through the orthogonality relations, the cross product terms with different values of k vanish and the integral may be written as follows.

$$\int_{t_1}^{t_2} \sum_k \left[\left(\frac{\partial \mathscr{L}_k''}{\partial \dot{y}_j} - \frac{d}{dt} \frac{\partial \mathscr{L}_k''}{\partial \ddot{y}_j} \right)^* \dot{\varphi}_{jk} - \left(\frac{\partial \mathscr{L}_k'}{\partial y_j} - \frac{d}{dt} \frac{\partial \mathscr{L}_k'}{\partial \dot{y}_j} \right)^* \dot{\varphi}_{jk} \right] dt = 0.$$

(501.19)

The following modification of (501.19) is obtained by substituting $i\omega_k \varphi_{jk}$ for $\dot{\varphi}_{jk}$ in the term on the right-hand side.

$$\int_{t_1}^{t_2} \sum_k \left[\left(\frac{\partial \mathscr{L}_k''}{\partial \dot{y}_j} - \frac{d}{dt} \frac{\partial \mathscr{L}_k''}{\partial \ddot{y}_j} \right)^* \dot{\varphi}_{jk} \right.$$

$$\left. - i\omega_k \left(\frac{\partial \mathscr{L}_k'}{\partial y_j} - \frac{d}{dt} \frac{\partial \mathscr{L}_k'}{\partial \dot{y}_j} \right)^* \varphi_{jk} \right] dt = 0$$ (501.20)

By reference to the relation cited in Chapter 2, Section 2.1.1 as (211.6), it is clear that (501.20) is equivalent to the following integral, the integrand of which consists entirely of real expressions, except for the factors $i\omega_k$.

$$2\int_{t_1}^{t_2}\sum_k\left[\left(\frac{\partial\mathcal{L}_k''}{\partial\dot{y}_j}-\frac{d}{dt}\frac{\partial\mathcal{L}_k''}{\partial\ddot{y}_j}\right)\dot{\varphi}_{jk}\right.$$
$$\left.-i\omega_k\left(\frac{\partial\mathcal{L}_k'}{\partial y_j}-\frac{d}{dt}\frac{\partial\mathcal{L}_k'}{\partial\dot{y}_j}\right)\varphi_{jk}\right]dt=0 \qquad (501.21)$$

Since $\mathcal{L}''$ is a function of $\dot{y}_j$ and $\ddot{y}_j$ while $\mathcal{L}'$ is a function of y_j and $\dot{y}_j$, it follows from (501.10), (501.11) and a well-known application of integration by parts, that (501.21) is merely the statement†

$$\delta\mathcal{P}_j^* = \sum_k\delta\mathcal{P}_{jk}^* = 0. \qquad (501.22)$$

It follows from (501.22) that as each partial variation in the *complex power* vanishes, therefore the total variation in the *complex power* must vanish.

$$\delta\mathcal{P}^* = \sum_j\delta\mathcal{P}_j^* = 0. \qquad (501.23)$$

Thus, by starting with (500.5) and showing that the variation of the *complex power* vanishes, and that the *complex power* is therefore stationary, we have proved that if the equations of motion (500.5) are satisfied, then the total *complex power* must

† It is implied here that $\delta\mathcal{P}_{jk}^*$ includes a term $[(\partial\mathcal{L}_k''/\partial\ddot{y}_j)\dot{\varphi}_{jk} - i\omega_k (\partial\mathcal{L}_k'/\partial\dot{y}_j)\varphi_{jk}]_{t_1}^{t_2}$ which vanishes. The imaginary part of this term vanishes because $\varphi_{jk}(t_1)$ and $\varphi_{jk}(t_2)$ vanish. In general $\dot{\varphi}_{jk}(t_1)$ and $\dot{\varphi}_{jk}(t_2)$ do not vanish, and therefore $\partial\mathcal{L}_k''/\partial\ddot{y}_j = \partial\Pi_k/\partial\ddot{y}_j$ must vanish at times $t = t_1$ and $t = t_2$. It may be seen that the latter requirement is not stringent, if we note that we are dealing from (501.13) to (501.23) with the system subject to no external forces, e.g., the requirement may be met with the coordinates given by the series $\gamma_j(t) = y_j(t_1) + \sum_k y_j(k)\sin(\omega_k t - \theta_k)$ with θ_k as given by (501.18) and with any choice of coefficients $y_j(k)$.

be stationary. As the system under consideration is linear, its behavior for one spectral component is independent of its behavior for another. It follows that *each* spectral component of the variation in the *complex power* $\delta\mathscr{P}_k{}^*$ must vanish separately, and therefore *each* spectral component of the *complex power* $\mathscr{P}_k{}^*$ must be stationary.

5.0.2. σ-Matrices and Green's Functions

The remainder of this chapter will be devoted primarily to the equations of motion themselves. This section will be concerned with certain general properties of linear systems, and the methods which one may use to assign the appropriate equations of motion to a given physical system will be treated in the following section. Consider the equations of motion (500.13) rewritten in the following form

$$S_{ij}y_j(t) = J_i(t), \qquad (502.1)$$

in which the elements of the secular matrix S_{ij} are the differential operators

$$S_{ij} = M_{ij}\frac{d^2}{dt^2} + R_{ij}\frac{d}{dt} + U_{ij}. \qquad (502.2)$$

The well-known *superposition theorem*, which was originally stated by Daniel Bernoulli as the *principle of the coexistence of small motions*, applies to the equations of motion (502.1).

Theorem IV *(the superposition theorem)*: If a set of forces $J_k'(t)$ gives the solutions $y_k'(t)$ of the equations of motion (502.1), and a different set of forces $J_k''(t)$ gives the solutions $y_k''(t)$, then it follows immediately from the linearity of (502.1) that a set of forces $J_k(t) = J_k'(t) + J_k''(t)$ gives the solution $y_j(t) = y_j'(t) + y_j''(t)$.

Proof: The relations

$$S_{ij}y_j'(t) = J_i'(t) \qquad (502.3)$$

and

$$S_{ij}y_j''(t) = J_i''(t) \qquad (502.4)$$

are given. Taking the sum of (502.3) and (502.4) gives

$$S_{ij}(y_j' + y_j'') = J_i' + J_i'', \qquad (502.5)$$

Q. E. D.

We are often interested in small excursions about an equilibrium configuration. Typical applications are servos operating about a preestablished reference position, or the dynamic fluctuations about the dc operating point of a transistor or vacuum tube. Such problems may be conveniently treated by a set of initial conditions which will be referred to as the *biased boundary conditions*. The equations of motion (502.1) are formally the same as (210.51). The transform of the latter (210.53) contains a term $p_i(\zeta, F_j(0), F_j'(0),...)$ which depends on the initial values of the coordinates and their derivatives. The biased boundary conditions are formulated in such a way that the term $p_i(\zeta, F_j(0), F_j'(0),...)$ in the transform of (502.1) vanishes, yet there is no sacrifice in the generality with which the initial conditions may be stated. Let the coordinates of the system be given by $x_j(t) = x_j(0) + y_j(t)$. We take as the independent variables of the problem $y_j(t)$ in order to make all the initial values of the coordinates vanish, at time $t = 0$, and, as $y_j(t)$ and $x_j(t)$ have the same time derivatives, the nature of the problem has been in no way changed by substituting $y_j(t)$ for $x_j(t)$. The method of handling the initial velocities is based on an argument given by Maxwell (1877). He pointed out that the time derivatives of the coordinates may undergo step-wise finite discontinuities when instantaneous impulses are delivered to the system. On the basis of his argument, an appropriate set of instantaneous impulses may be delivered to the system at time $t = 0$ to produce the desired set of initial velocities. Hence, we apply the superposition theorem and rewrite (502.1) as

$$S_{ij}y_j(t) = J_i''(t) + J_i'(t), \qquad (502.6)$$

with $J_i'(t)$ chosen so as to produce the proper initial velocities, and $J_i''(t)$ to represent the external forces applied to the system. We write for the instantaneous impulses

$$J_i'(t) = A_i\,\delta(t), \qquad (502.7)$$

in which the constants A_i must be determined to yield the proper initial velocities. This is done by substituting the impulses (502.7) into the equations of motion (502.1) and integrating with respect to the time between the limits 0 and Δt. The result may be written

$$\lim_{\Delta t \to 0} \int_0^{\Delta t} S_{ij}y_j\,dt = A_i \int_0^\infty \delta(t)\,dt = A_i, \qquad (502.8)$$

which reduces, by Maxwell's argument, to the expression

$$A_i = M_{ij} \lim_{\Delta t \to 0} \left[\dot{y}_j(\Delta t) - \dot{y}_j(0) \right], \qquad (502.9)$$

$$A_i = M_{ij}\,\Delta\dot{y}_j(0). \qquad (502.10)$$

The initial velocities are, of course, given by the increments $\Delta\dot{y}_j(0)$. Hence, by substituting (502.10) in (502.7), we obtain, as Maxwell's instantaneous impulses, the relations

$$J_i'(t) = M_{ij}\,\Delta\dot{y}_j(0)\,\delta(t). \qquad (502.11)$$

We now substitute (502.11) in (502.6), then multiply through by $e^{-\zeta t}$ and integrate with respect to the time over the limits 0 to ∞. The result may be written

$$s_{ij}(\zeta)Y_j(\zeta) = M_{ij}\,\Delta\dot{y}_j(0) + j_i(\zeta), \qquad (502.12)$$

in which the elements of the new secular matrix are the following quadratic expressions

$$s_{ij}(\zeta) = M_{ij}\zeta^2 + R_{ij}\zeta + U_{ij}. \tag{502.13}$$

The factors $Y_j(\zeta)$ in (502.12) are the transforms of the functions to be determined, e.g.,

$$\Xi\, y_j(t) = Y_j(\zeta), \tag{502.14}$$

and $j_i(\zeta)$ represent the transforms of the given forces $J_i''(t)$, or

$$\Xi\, J_i''(t) = j_i(\zeta). \tag{210.55}$$

We now introduce the σ-matrix of the system, which is the inverse of the secular matrix $s_{ij}(\zeta)$ as defined by the relation

$$\sigma_{jk}(\zeta)s_{ki} = \delta_{ji}. \tag{210.58}$$

Multiplying both sides of (502.12) on the left-hand side by the square σ-matrix gives the expression

$$Y_j(\zeta) = \sigma_{jk}(\zeta)\left[M_{km}\,\Delta\dot{y}_m(0) + j_k(\zeta)\right]. \tag{502.15}$$

Let $\Sigma_{jk}(t)$ denote the inverse transforms of the corresponding elements of the σ-matrix, or

$$\Xi\, \Sigma_{jk}(t) = \sigma_{jk}(\zeta). \tag{210.60}$$

The Green's functions of the system, $\Sigma_{jk}(t)$, play a very important role in its behavior, as may be seen in the following expression for the solution of (502.15), which follows immediately from the relation (210.50) between the convolution of two functions and the product of their transforms.

$$y_j(t) = M_{km}\,\Delta\dot{y}_m(0)\,\Sigma_{jk}(t) + \int_0^t \Sigma_{jk}(t-\tau)J_k''(\tau)\,d\tau. \tag{502.16}$$

The first term on the right-hand side of (502.16) may be recognized as the *transient solution*. The second term on the right-hand side of (502.16) gives the response of the system to the applied forces, and if these forces are periodic then it is called the *steady state solution*. It is important to distinguish the difference between the contributions to the solution by the functions $J_k''(t)$ and the factors $M_{km}\,\Delta\dot{y}_m(0)$ as opposed to the Green's functions $\Sigma_{jk}(t)$. The important distinction is that the Green's functions $\Sigma_{jk}(t)$ are characteristic of the system, while both $J_k''(t)$ and $M_{km}\,\Delta\dot{y}_m(0)$ depend on arbitrary choices of the applied forces and initial velocities respectively. Therefore, the Green's functions contain all the natural modes of motion of the system. As it is always possible, in principle, to take the convolution indicated in (502.16) to treat any particular choice of forces $J_k''(t)$, one has essentially obtained a general solution for the behavior of a system by obtaining its Green's functions $\Sigma_{jk}(t)$.

A physical interpretation of the Green's functions may be obtained by allowing the integral on the right-hand side of (502.16) to represent the response of the system at rest to an impulse delivered along one of its branches at time $t = 0$. This is accomplished by expressing the functions $J_k''(t)$ in the following form

$$J_k''(t) = 0, \qquad k \neq s, \qquad J_s''(t) = \delta(t), \qquad (502.17)$$

which designates the coordinate $y_s(t)$ as the one along which the impulse is to be delivered. Inserting (502.17) into the integral on the right-hand side of (502.16) gives at once

$$y_j(t) = \Sigma_{js}(t). \qquad (502.18)$$

Hence, the response of the jth coordinate in the system following an impulse delivered along the sth coordinate is the Green's function $\Sigma_{js}(t)$. It follows at once from the principle of *causality* that the response of the system to the impulse cannot precede it, and hence we have the general statement $\Sigma_{js}(t) = 0$, $t < 0$.

The methods of solving the equations of motion of a system which are outlined here have been commonly treated in the literature. The methods are somewhat more common than the terminology, e.g., following the precedent established by James and Weiss (1947) what we have called the Green's function $\Sigma_{js}(t)$ is sometimes called the *weighting function*, and its transform the $\sigma_{js}(\zeta)$ element of the σ-matrix is called the *transfer function*.

Consider the steady state response of the system to a single sinusoidal force applied along the sth coordinate, which may be treated by letting $J_i'(t)$ vanish in (502.6), and representing the applied forces by the following simple expression.

$$J_k''(t) = 0, \qquad k \neq s, \qquad J_s''(t) = e^{i\omega t}. \qquad (502.19)$$

The solution, which is readily obtained, may be written

$$y_j(t) = \sigma_{js}(i\omega) e^{i\omega t}. \qquad (502.20)$$

Hence, the ac amplitude of the sinusoidal motion of the jth coordinate, produced by a sinusoidal excitation of the sth coordinate, is the $\sigma_{js}(i\omega)$ element of the σ-matrix of the system. Thus, we have seen that both the Green's functions matrix and its transform, the σ-matrix, have the simple physical interpretations given by (502.18) and (502.20) respectively. Consider the steady state behavior resulting from a solitary periodic force confined to the sth coordinate of the system; e.g., we let

$$J_k''(t) = 0, \qquad k \neq s, \qquad J_s''(t) = \sum_{-\infty}^{\infty} j_n e^{in\omega t}. \qquad (502.21)$$

It follows from the superposition theorem and (502.21) that the result may be written immediately as

$$y_j(t) = \sum_{-\infty}^{\infty} j_n \sigma_{js}(in\omega) e^{in\omega t}. \qquad (502.22)$$

As the periodic behavior of the system is implicitly contained in the simple ac expression (502.20), the latter is often made to represent the normalized typical term of a Fourier series in order to avoid the additional complexity of the notation of (502.22).

As the equations of motion (502.1) come from a Lagrangian which is quadratic in the coordinates and velocities, it immediately follows that the secular matrix S_{ij} is symmetric, and it also follows from the symmetry of the secular matrix that its transform s_{ij}, the σ-matrix, and the Green's function matrix Σ_{ij}, are all symmetric. As the characteristic behavior of the system is determined by these matrices, one might expect their symmetry to be manifest somehow in the behavior. This is evident in the *reciprocity theorem* which stems from the symmetry of the square S-, s-, σ- and Σ-matrices. This theorem has many applications; Helmholtz applied it in acoustics, and Lord Rayleigh treated it quite generally. Some salient points on the theorem have been made by Casimir (1963).

Theorem V *(the reciprocity theorem)*: The response of the jth coordinate to a force applied to the sth coordinate is the same as the response of the sth coordinate to the same force applied to the jth coordinate for any physical system whose Lagrangian is quadratic in the coordinates and velocities.

Proof (for a periodic force): The force applied along the sth coordinate is represented by (502.19) and the response to that force by the jth coordinate is given by (502.20). The same force applied along the jth coordinate is expressed

$$J(t_k'') = 0, \qquad k \neq j, \qquad J_j''(t) = e^{i\omega t}. \qquad (502.23)$$

The corresponding solution may be written

$$y_s(t) = \sigma_{sj}(i\omega)e^{i\omega t}. \qquad (502.24)$$

As the σ-matrix is symmetric, so that $\sigma_{js}(i\omega)$ equals $\sigma_{sj}(i\omega)$, then $y_j(t)$ in (502.20) equals $y_s(t)$ in (502.24).

Q. E. D.

Proof (for an aperiodic force): An impulse is delivered along the sth coordinate as indicated by (502.17), and the corresponding response of the jth coordinate by (502.18). Then by applying the convolution integral of (502.16) the response to any particular aperiodic force may be obtained. In order to apply the same force along the jth coordinate, we write for an impulse

$$J_k''(t) = 0, \qquad k \neq j, \qquad J_j''(t) = \delta(t). \qquad (502.25)$$

which has the solution

$$y_s(t) = \Sigma_{sj}(t). \qquad (502.26)$$

As the matrix of the Green's functions is symmetric so that $\Sigma_{js}(t) = \Sigma_{sj}(t)$ it follows that $y_s(t)$ in (502.26) equals $y_j(t)$ in (502.18), and, more generally, the convolution in (502.16) makes this equality hold for any aperiodic force applied first along the sth coordinate and then along the jth coordinate.

Q. E. D.

In the discussion of the physical interpretation of the elements of the σ- and Σ-matrices and in the proof of the reciprocity theorem, we have examined the response of any coordinate in the system to a solitary force applied along just one coordinate. In treating physical systems we frequently specify the force and the coordinate along which it is applied as the *input force* and the *input coordinate*, and select some other coordinate of particular interest in the system and specify it as the *output coordinate*. This leads to a convenient method of treating the system in which, for generality, we introduce a second force along the output coordinate which vanishes in many applications. The method which follows reduces the treatment to that for a system of two independent coordinates, and so, when the system is being considered in this sense, it will be referred to as the *reduced system*. In the special case of electric circuits, the reduced system is a *four-terminal network*. For the system under discussion, it follows from (502.20) that the solution of the equations of motion may be written

$$y_1(t) = \sigma_{11}(i\omega)j_1 e^{i\omega t} + \sigma_{1n}(i\omega)j_n e^{i\omega t},$$
$$y_n(t) = \sigma_{n1}(i\omega)j_1 e^{i\omega t} + \sigma_{nn}(i\omega)j_n e^{i\omega t},$$

(502.27)

or, in matrix form,

$$\begin{pmatrix} y_1 \\ y_n \end{pmatrix} = \begin{pmatrix} \sigma_{11} & \sigma_{1n} \\ \sigma_{n1} & \sigma_{nn} \end{pmatrix} \begin{pmatrix} j_1 \\ j_n \end{pmatrix} e^{i\omega t}.$$

(502.28)

The σ-matrix in (502.28) is designated here as the *reduced σ-matrix*. Multiplying both sides of (502.28) on the left by the reciprocal of the reduced σ-matrix gives the equations of motion of the reduced system, viz.,

$$\begin{pmatrix} s'_{11} & s'_{1n} \\ s'_{n1} & s'_{nn} \end{pmatrix} \begin{pmatrix} y_1 \\ y_n \end{pmatrix} = \begin{pmatrix} j_1 \\ j_n \end{pmatrix} e^{i\omega t},$$

(502.29)

with

$$s'_{11} = \frac{\sigma_{nn}}{|\sigma_{ij}|}, \quad s'_{nn} = \frac{\sigma_{11}}{|\sigma_{ij}|}, \quad s'_{1n} = s'_{n1} = \frac{-\sigma_{1n}}{|\sigma_{ij}|}.$$

(502.30)

It is often convenient to treat a complicated system as one with just two independent coordinates in terms of (502.29), especially if the elements of the reduced secular matrix are to be measured experimentally rather than calculated.

Sometimes the coordinates are interrelated through non-holonomic conditions, as discussed in Chapter 4, Section 4.1, and it is necessary to treat the velocities as the independent variables. It is common practice to assume from the outset that this may be the case, and, when the solution finally appears, if certain coordinates are clearly defined, to obtain them by integrating their respective velocities. In order to outline this method, it is convenient to introduce the operator $(d/dt)^{-1}$ which is defined by

$$(d/dt)^{-1} y(t) = \int_0^t y(\tau) \, d\tau.$$

(502.31)

When the velocities replace the coordinates as the independent variables, then the elements of the secular matrix are written

$$S_{ij} = M_{ij}(d/dt) + R_{ij} + U_{ij}(d/dt)^{-1}. \qquad (502.32)$$

Hence, the transform of the equations of motion has a secular matrix whose elements are given by the following relation.

$$s_{ij}(\zeta) = M_{ij}\zeta + R_{ij} + U_{ij}\zeta^{-1}. \qquad (502.33)$$

The secular matrix for the ac response of the system is obtained by replacing ζ in (502.33) by $i\omega$, and with electric circuits, the elements of the secular matrix are *impedances*. The use of the impedance has been extended by analogy to rotating electrical machinery by Kron (1935, 1959), to mechanical, acoustic, and hydraulic problems by Olson (1943, 1947) and others as summarized by Firestone (1957). In engineering, it is not unusual to treat a physical system containing three different kinds of coordinates, e.g., mechanical, electromagnetic, and hydraulic, or mechanical, electromagnetic, and acoustic, etc.

Clearly a compact electrical network composed of coils, capacitors, and resistances may have the same equations of motion as a large and unwieldy mechanical system, apart from simple conversion factors. Such an electric network may be used to study the behavior of a large mechanical system which would be more expensive to construct. Electric networks which are employed in this manner are called *analog computers*. Analog computers may be made to time the steps in a chemical process, solve problems in navigation, etc.

5.0.3. Electrical Systems

The equations of motion of some nonconservative electromagnetic networks are treated in this section. We commence by recalling two important conclusions that were stated in Chapter 4, viz., that the equations of motion are a statement of Kirchhoff's voltage law, and that the nonholonomic conditions between interrelated coordinates are given by Kirchhoff's current law. In the treatment of electrical networks, it is common practice to follow a set of conventions in assigning the currents and voltages on the circuit diagram in such a way as to give independent currents automatically, thereby eliminating the equations of condition. Before stating these conventions, some remarks will be made about the terms charge and voltage as applied to electromagnetic networks.

At first glance, it might seem ambiguous to refer to charge in the customary sense and also as a coordinate; the property of a direction which is inherently required of a coordinate seems discordant with the familiar concept of charge as a scalar quantity. For essentially the same reason, the use of voltage to represent a force seems out of harmony with the familiar concept of potential as a scalar. However, the use of these terms in electrical networks is indeed proper and consistent.

In electromagnetic systems which may be treated by circuits, the charge q refers to the charge on a conducting body, e.g., a charge $+q$ appears on a conductor in Fig. 5.3. It may be assumed that the lines of force emanating from the positive charge terminate on a neighboring conductor which has the charge $-q$. These two conductors may be treated as a capacitance if their separation is small compared with the product of the period of the charge fluctuations and the velocity of light. The charge is applied to one conductor through a terminal marked a, and to the other conductor through a terminal marked b. The direction of q as a coordinate corresponds to the direction in which positive charge flows in charging the capacitance. If positive charge flows in at terminal a and out at terminal b, the direction of q is positive, and if positive charge flows in at b and out at a, the direction of the charge is negative. As with any other kind of coordinate, the choice is arbitrary in the assignment of positive and negative directions; in the example given here we arbitrarily assign the positive direction of q to make positive charge flow in at a and out at b. The circuit representation for this system is shown in Fig. 5.4a. Consider a slightly more complicated system in which a conductor has positive charge, but the lines of the electric field emanating from that body terminate on two neigh-

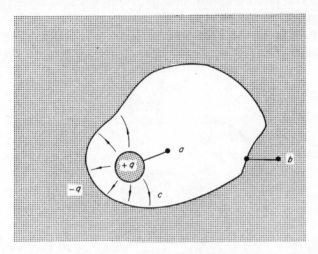

Fig. 5.3. Schematic diagram of two neighboring conductors with equal but opposite charge.

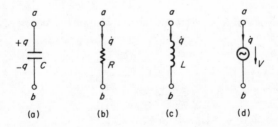

Fig. 5.4. Schematic circuit diagrams: (a) capacitor, (b) resistor, (c) inductance, (d) generator.

boring conductors rather than one, as shown in Fig. 5.5a. Two capacitors C_1 and C_2 are required in this system, as indicated in Fig. 5.5a. The conventional circuit diagram of the system is shown in Fig. 5.5b.

The flow of current $\dot{q}$ in a resistance and in an inductance is shown schematically in Fig. 5.4b and c respectively, and in both cases we take the current flow from a toward b as being positive, and the flow from b to a as negative.

Each independent current $\dot{q}_i$ corresponds to a closed loop in the circuit, so that by designating the minimum number of loops

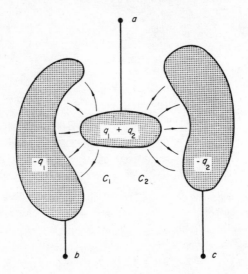

Fig. 5.5a.   Three neighboring charged conductors.

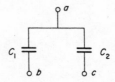

Fig. 5.5b.   Conventional circuit diagram representing the three conductors in Fig. 5.5a.

that can account for the current in each branch of the network one has selected the independent coordinates. It may be shown that the current is the same in those branches of the ith loop that are not common with other branches, and it is evident that the flow indicated on a plane diagram must be either clockwise or counter-clockwise with respect to the ith loop. A clockwise arrow is drawn at the center of the ith loop with $\dot{q}_i$ at its center, to indicate that the clockwise direction of the current $\dot{q}_i$ is taken

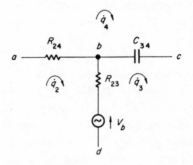

Fig. 5.6. Branch point b of a circuit diagram.

to be positive, and to indicate that in those branches which are common with other loops $\dot{q}_i$ is the component of the current contributed by the ith loop. By designating the currents in this way, it follows that, at any branch point of the network, Kirchhoff's current law is automatically satisfied, because the current that flows toward the point consists of the contributions of the connecting loops each of which enters and leaves so that the total must vanish. A typical branch point is designated b in Fig. 5.6. The current flow to the branch point b is contributed by the second, third, and fourth loops. The current flow from a to b is $\dot{q}_2 - \dot{q}_4$, that from c to b is $\dot{q}_4 - \dot{q}_3$, and that from d to b is $\dot{q}_3 - \dot{q}_2$, the sum of which vanishes. Hence, the rule for designating currents may be generalized as follows.

Electrical Circuit Convention I *(the rules for designating currents as independent variables)*: The positive direction of the current $\dot{q}_i$ is taken to be clockwise in the ith loop. The current $\dot{q}_i$ flows in the branches common only to the ith loop, the current $\dot{q}_i - \dot{q}_j$ flows in the branch common to the ith and jth loops, the current $\dot{q}_i - \dot{q}_j - \dot{q}_k$ flows in the branch common to the ith, jth, and kth loops, etc.

As is customary with electrical networks, we regard the currents $\dot{q}_i$ as the independent variables, making the secular matrix an impedance matrix with elements of the general form given by relation (502.32). Hence, we write the equations of motion

$$Z_{ij}\dot{q}_j = V_i. \tag{503.1}$$

A voltage generator is shown schematically in Fig. 5.4d, applying a force V along the coordinate q; the positive direction of the voltage V is indicated by the arrow which points in the direction that positive charge flows in response to a positive value of V; the magnitude of V is the potential difference between terminals a and b, i.e., taking V_a and V_b as the scalar potentials at terminals a and b, we have $|V| = V_b - V_a$ for the magnitude of the voltage V. Figure 5.7 shows a series RC circuit connected to a generator. The sign of the charge q on the capacitance and the flow of the current $\dot{q}$ agree with the direction assigned to the voltage applied by the generator. Figure 5.7 illustrates a one-dimensional example in which the force V has been applied along the coordinate q.

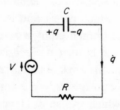

Fig. 5.7. Schematic diagram of a series RC circuit.

If a generator is connected in a branch of the network that is common with two or more loops, then that generator applies a voltage either in the same direction as, or in the opposite direction to, each of the coordinates associated with the common loops. For example, in Fig. 5.6, a generator is connected in the branch $d-b$, and that branch is common to the second and third loops; in this example the generator applies a voltage V_b in the direction of the velocity $\dot{q}_3$ and opposite to the velocity $\dot{q}_2$. Voltage generators are treated on circuit diagrams according to the following rule.

Electrical Circuit Convention II: The voltage applied by a generator is designated by two symbols, an arrow and V. If a generator is connected in a branch of a circuit which is common only to the ith loop, then the voltage V appears only in the equation of (503.1) which contains Z_{ii}, and it is positive if the arrow points in the same direction as $\dot{q}_i$, but it is negative if the arrow points opposite to $\dot{q}_i$. Similarly, if a generator is connected in a branch of the circuit which is common with the ith, jth, and kth loops, then the voltage V appears in the three equations of (503.1) which contain Z_{ii}, Z_{jj}, and Z_{kk} respectively, and its sign depends on whether the arrow points in the same direction as or opposite to the currents $\dot{q}_i$, $\dot{q}_j$, and $\dot{q}_k$ respectively.

Of course, the component of current $\dot{q}_i$ may flow counterclockwise rather than clockwise as indicated on the circuit diagram, and, if this is the case, then the solution for $\dot{q}_i$ has a negative sign. More generally, with the ac case, the phase factors of the currents indicate to what degree they are synchronized with the voltages applied by the generators.

A theorem is now stated for electrical networks in which the currents are the independent variables.

Theorem VI: The diagonal element of the impedance matrix Z_{ii} refers to the ith loop of the circuit and gives the total impedance of that loop, and the off-diagonal element Z_{ij} $(i \neq j)$ refers to that branch of the ith network which is common with the jth loop and is minus one times the impedance of that branch.

A bibliography of the literature on the analysis of electrical circuits by topological methods has been listed by Gardner and Barnes (1942). Conventions I and II will be applied to two simple examples which will serve to verify Theorem VI. The first example is the electrical circuit illustrated in Fig. 5.8. There

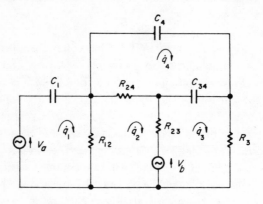

Fig. 5.8.   Schematic circuit diagram.

are four loops in this circuit, and therefore there are four, equations of motion (503.1), with $i = 1, 2, 3, 4$, and $j = 1, 2, 3, 4$. According to Convention II, the applied voltages to be used in the equations of motion (503.1) may be written

$$V_1(t) = V_a(t), \quad V_2(t) = -V_b(t),$$
$$V_3(t) = V_b(t), \quad V_4(t) = 0, \tag{503.2}$$

By inserting (503.2) into (503.1) and selecting the elements of the impedance matrix so as to make the four equations of motion correspond to Kirchhoff's voltage law for each of the four loops, one obtains the following matrix elements

$$Z_{11} = R_{12} + \frac{1}{C_1}\left(\frac{d}{dt}\right)^{-1}, \quad Z_{12} = -R_{12}, \quad Z_{13} = Z_{14} = 0,$$

$$Z_{22} = R_{12} + R_{23} + R_{24}, \quad Z_{23} = -R_{23}, \quad Z_{24} = -R_{24},$$

$$Z_{34} = -\frac{1}{C_{34}}\left(\frac{d}{dt}\right)^{-1}, \quad Z_{33} = R_3 + R_{23} + \frac{1}{C_{34}}\left(\frac{d}{dt}\right)^{-1}, \quad (503.3)$$

$$Z_{44} = R_{24} + \left(\frac{1}{C_4} + \frac{1}{C_{34}}\right)\left(\frac{d}{dt}\right)^{-1}.$$

It should not be stated merely that the result (503.3) agrees with Theorem VI, but it should be pointed out also that by that theorem and the circuit diagram, the elements (503.3) may be written at once by inspection.

The coupling between the jth and the kth circuit loops is given by the off-diagonal element of the impedance matrix Z_{jk}, as given by Theorem VI, and, in order to illustrate how that part of the theorem should be applied to coupled coils, the equations

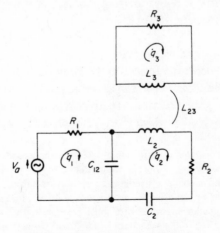

Fig. 5.9.   Schematic circuit diagram.

of motion for another special case will be considered. Take as an example the electrical circuit which is schematically sketched in Fig. 5.9. That circuit contains two inductances, L_2 and L_3, which are coupled by a mutual inductance L_{23}. In this instance, the off-diagonal impedance elements which couple circuit loops two and three are written $Z_{23} = - L_{23} d/dt$.[†] Hence, we have from Theorem VI, for the elements of the impedance matrix,

$$Z_{11} = R_{11} + \frac{1}{C_{12}}\left(\frac{d}{dt}\right)^{-1}, \quad Z_{12} = -\frac{1}{C_{12}}\left(\frac{d}{dt}\right)^{-1}, \quad Z_{13} = 0,$$

$$Z_{22} = L_2\frac{d}{dt} + R_2 + \left(\frac{1}{C_2} + \frac{1}{C_{12}}\right)\left(\frac{d}{dt}\right)^{-1}, \quad (503.4)$$

$$Z_{23} = -L_{13}\frac{d}{dt}, \quad Z_{33} = L_3\frac{d}{dt} + R_3,$$

and, from Convention II for the elements of the voltage matrix

$$V_1(t) = V_a(t), \quad V_2(t) = V_3(t) = 0. \quad (503.5)$$

One may verify that by inserting (503.4) and (503.5) into the equations of motion (503.1), Kirchhoff's voltage relations are obtained.

The treatment of electromagnetic systems by Conventions I and II, and Theorem VI is called the *mesh analysis* by electrical engineers. The term, the nth mesh is frequently used to denote the nth loop in the literature. There is another equally effective method of analysis in which (503.1) is replaced by the following

[†] We assume here that the direction of current in the secondary winding is assigned to make $Z_{23} = - L_{23}\,d/dt$ rather than $Z_{23} = + L_{23}\,d/dt$. If either the primary and secondary windings share current through a common section, as in an autotransformer, or a coil is coupled through more than one mutual inductance, special care must be exercised in assigning the direction of current in the secondary winding and the sign of the mutual inductance (see Exercises 5.14 and 5.15).

relation

$$Y_{ij}V_j = \dot{q}_i \qquad (503.6)$$

as the original statement of the problem. In this treatment, which is often called *node analysis*,[†] the currents $\dot{q}_i$ are given functions of the time, and the voltages V_j are to be determined. The elements of the Y-matrix are the admittances of certain branches of the network. For reasons cited earlier in connection with the impedance matrix Z_{ij}, the admittance matrix Y_{ij} is symmetric.

With the node analysis, one node is arbitrarily designated as a reference node, and the other nodes in the network identify the independent variables (voltages) of the problem. By designating a voltage to each node, Kirchoff's voltage law is automatically satisfied, and (503.6) is a statement of Kirchhoff's current law.

A diagram of a circuit which is suitable for the node analysis is shown in Fig. 5.10. This circuit has three *separable parts*, i.e., apart from coupling through mutual inductance three parts of the network are otherwise isolated from each other. A reference node in each of the separable parts has been arbitrarily designated by 0 and grounded. The remaining ten nodes have been numbered, and the voltages V_i, $i = 1, 2,\ldots, 10$, represent the potential difference between the ith node and the grounded reference node.

We appear to have sacrificed generality here by grounding the reference node in each of the separable parts of the network. However, the circuit diagram of a system is an approximation which takes into account the dominant electromagnetic inter-

---

[†] Physicists have been slow in accepting this usage of the term *node*. Having used it already with lines of nodes in Keplerian motion, and the nodal lines of a vibrating membrane, there has been perhaps some hesitance in applying the same word to a branch point in an electrical network. However, when gauged by the broad usage of the word *node*, particularly with reference to botany and geometry, its customary application to electrical networks by engineers is quite appropriate.

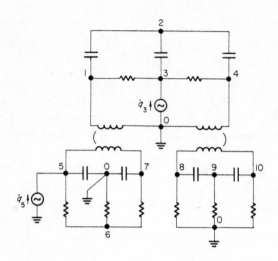

Fig. 5.10.   Schematic circuit diagram.

actions and entirely omits the interaction between parts of the
system which are very weakly coupled. There is, of course, some
electromagnetic coupling between the separable parts of the
network in addition to that by transformer coupling, and the
influence of this additional coupling becomes more important
with increasing frequency. With the high frequency interactions
properly accounted for on the circuit diagram, there are no
separable parts of the circuit. By grounding the reference nodes
in each of the separable parts of the circuit, as shown in Fig. 5.10,
those interactions that have been omitted in the diagram are
subdued.

Obviously the same circuit always may be represented by
either a node or mesh network, but this does not necessarily
mean that the impedance matrix Z_{ij} in (503.1) is the reciprocal of
the admittance matrix Y_{ij} in (503.6), because the currents $\dot{q}_j$
and voltages V_i in (503.1) and (503.6) do not generally refer
to the same quantities. With the node analysis the voltage V_j

becomes a coordinate (it is no longer a force), and it gives the scalar potential of the jth node in the network. Whether V_j is positive or negative depends on whether it is above or below the potential of the reference node. In the node analysis the currents are no longer velocities, but become forces, i.e., a current source plays an analogous role to that of the voltage generator in the mesh analysis. A voltage generator (Fig. 5.11a)

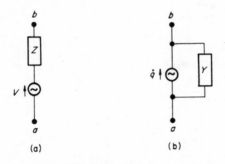

Fig. 5.11.   (a) Voltage generator. (b) Current source.

is characterized not only by its voltage $V\uparrow$, but also by its series impedance Z which must appear in the impedance elements of the meshes in which it is connected. Similarly, a current source is characterized by its current $\dot{q}\uparrow$, and also by the shunt admittance Y across its terminals (Fig. 5.11b). A current source may be substituted for a voltage generator in a circuit according to the following theorem, the proof of which is left as an exercise for the reader.

Theorem VII: A generator with voltage $V\uparrow$ and series impedance Z is equivalent to a current source with current $\dot{q}\uparrow$ and shunt admittance Y, if the arrows point in the same direction, $\dot{q} = V/Z$, and $Y = Z^{-1}$.

A current source is always connected between two nodes. If a current source connects two nodes, neither of which is the reference node, it may be replaced by two sources each node being connected to one of the two sources and the opposite terminal of each source being connected to the reference node. Hence, generality is not sacrificed by connecting one terminal of each current source to the reference node, a practice which is followed here. Fig. 5.12 shows the nth node of a circuit, (a) with

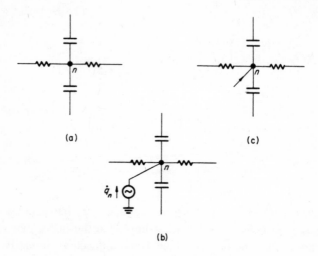

Fig. 5.12.   Schematic circuit diagram.

no current source, (b) with a current source as indicated conventionally, and (c) also with a current source but indicated by a convention used here.

The conventions customarily used with the node analysis may be summarized as follows.

Electrical Circuit Convention III *(the rules for designating voltages as independent variables)*: In each separable part of a network one node is grounded and the remaining nodes are

numbered $i = 1, 2, 3,\ldots,n$. The voltage of the ith node, designated V_i, represents the potential difference between the ith
node and ground.

Electrical Circuit Convention IV: A generator is represented as
a current source by Theorem VII. A current source is connected
between ground and the typical nth node as shown in Figure
5.12b and c. When $\dot{q}_n$ is positive the source delivers current to
the nth node in the direction required to make V_n become more
positive.

The following theorem plays the same role with the node
analysis as Theorem VI in the mesh analysis.

Theorem VIII: The diagonal element of the Y-matrix refers to
the ith node of the circuit and gives the total admittance connected to that node, and the off-diagonal element Y_{ij} $(i \neq j)$
refers to the connecting branch between the ith and jth nodes
and is minus one times the admittance of that branch.

We will now obtain the appropriate elements of the admittance
and current matrices in (503.6) by applying Conventions III and
IV to two examples in order to illustrate the method of the node
analysis and to verify Theorem VIII for two special cases.
Consider the schematic circuit diagram in Fig. 5.13. The network has only one separable part, and so the grounded node

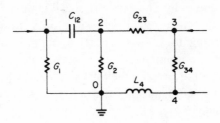

Fig. 5.13.   Schematic circuit diagram.

marked 0 is the only reference node. As there are four remaining nodes, the system has four equations of the form (503.6), and the solution of those four equations gives the voltages of the four nodes which are designated according to Convention III. The currents $\dot{q}_i$ are given functions which are assigned to conform with Convention IV, and by that convention and the inspection of Fig. 5.13, it may be seen that $\dot{q}_2$ vanishes, and that $\dot{q}_1$, $\dot{q}_3$, and $\dot{q}_4$ must be specified, e.g.,

$$\dot{q}_2 = 0, \quad \dot{q}_i \neq 0, \quad i = 1, 3, 4. \tag{503.7}$$

By applying Kirchhoff's current law to the network (Fig. 5.13), one obtains four relations which may be written by (503.6) and (503.7) by writing the admittance elements in (503.6) as indicated below.

$$Y_{11} = G_1 + C_{12}(d/dt), \quad Y_{22} = G_2 + G_{23} + C_{12}(d/dt),$$
$$Y_{33} = G_{23} + G_{34}, \quad Y_{44} = G_{34} + L_4^{-1}(d/dt)^{-1},$$
$$Y_{12} = -C_{12}(d/dt), \quad Y_{23} = -G_{23}, \tag{503.8}$$
$$Y_{34} = -G_{34}, \quad Y_{13} = Y_{14} = Y_{24} = 0.$$

The application of Kirchhoff's current law to the circuit (Fig. 5.13) verifies Theorem VIII, as the admittance elements (503.8) may be written by Theorem VIII and Fig. 5.13 by inspection.

The method of node analysis will be applied to the circuit shown in Fig. 5.8 which has been used to illustrate the method of mesh analysis. The generators in Fig. 5.8 may be converted to current sources by Theorem VII, and Figure 5.14 shows the network of the same system redrawn in order to designate the nodes according to Convention III and the current sources according to Convention IV. The appropriate currents to be used in (503.6) are given by the following relations in which the symbols on the left-hand side refer to Fig. 5.14 and those on the right-hand side to Fig. 5.8.

$$\dot{q}_1 = C_1(dV_a/dt), \quad \dot{q}_2 = V_b/R_{23}, \quad \dot{q}_3 = 0. \tag{503.9}$$

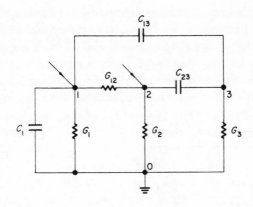

Fig. 5.14. Node network equivalent to the mesh network shown in Fig. 5.8.

The relations between the circuit symbols in the two figures are listed below with the symbols for Fig. 5.14 on the left-hand side of each equation, and those for Fig. 5.8 on the right-hand side.

$$C_1 = C_1 \qquad G_{12} = R_{24}^{-1} \qquad C_{23} = C_{34}$$
$$G_2 = R_{23}^{-1} \qquad G_1 = R_{12}^{-1} \qquad C_{13} = C_4 \qquad (503.10)$$
$$G_3 = R_3^{-1}$$

By applying Kirchhoff's current law to the network (Fig. 5.14) one obtains three linear equations in the form of (503.6) in which the currents $\dot{q}_i$ are given by (503.9) and the admittance elements Y_{ij} by the following relations.

$$Y_{11} = G_1 + G_{12} + (C_1 + C_{13})(d/dt), \quad Y_{12} = -G_{12},$$
$$Y_{13} = -C_{13}(d/dt), \quad Y_{22} = G_2 + G_{12} + C_{23}(d/dt), \quad (503.11)$$
$$Y_{23} = -C_{23}(d/dt), \quad Y_{33} = G_3 + (C_{13} + C_{23})(d/dt).$$

Hence, Theorem VIII has once more been verified, as the admittance elements (503.11) may be written by Theorem VIII and Figure 5.14 by inspection. It should be emphasized that four equations must be solved to treat this example by the mesh analysis, and only three with the node analysis.

Any network that will yield to the node analysis may be broken down into a four-terminal network by the arguments used in connection with (502.27)–(502.30). It is desirable to use both the mesh and the node methods interchangeably, and this requires the addition of one more circuit convention to make the four-terminal representation consistent with both methods. The output coordinate and force have been designated as y_n and J_n respectively in (502.27)–(502.30). It is customary in the four-terminal representation of electrical circuits to replace the input and output coordinates by their respective velocities, and to replace the ouput velocity $\dot{q}_n$ and output voltage v_n by $\dot{q}_2$ and v_2 respectively. The conventional diagram of a four-terminal network is shown in Fig. 5.15. The customary repre-

Fig. 5.15.   Schematic diagram of a four-terminal network.

sentation of the output current is consistent with the node analysis by conforming with Convention IV, and it is inconsistent with the mesh analysis as its direction is opposite to that required by Convention I. Hence, to make the mesh analysis applicable to the conventional four-terminal network, the output current and output voltage must both be multiplied by -1. It is left as an exercise for the reader to show that this convention has only the effect of reversing the signs of the off-diagonal elements in the σ-matrix (502.27)–(502.30).

Electrical Circuit Convention V: The positive directions of the input and output currents and voltages of a four-terminal network, indicated in Fig. 5.15, are consistent with the node analysis; the input current and voltage are also consistent with the mesh analysis, but the output current and voltage with the mesh analysis must both be multiplied by -1 to agree with the output current and voltage of the standard four-terminal network.

Of the theorems on electrical circuits, that by Thevenin is one of the most useful. It will be discussed here for the ac case. Thevenin's theorem is used to determine the behavior of a particular impedance, Z_n, which is considered as the output impedance of a network. Thevenin's theorem gives a rule by which the entire network is replaced by a generator connected to the output impedance Z_n. Although Thevenin's theorem is most commonly applied to electrical circuits, it is valid for all linear physical systems, and even more, it is intimately related to their fundamental properties. For example, it is frequently convenient to redefine the boundaries of a physical system so as to exclude part of the original system and account for its interaction through one or more external forces applied to the remaining system. Thevenin's theorem gives a systematic rule for doing just that.

Theorem IX *(Thevenin's theorem)*: If an impedance Z_n is connected between two points of a network, the resulting current through this impedance is the ratio of the potential difference between the two points prior to the connection of Z_n, to the sum of Z_n and Z, the impedance of the network measured between the two points.

Thevenin's Theorem says that any network acts like a generator. Thus, to determine the current fed to Z_n, either by a network or a generator, one first disconnects Z_n and measures the open circuit voltage V; then one turns off the generator and measures the impedance Z across the terminals from which Z_n has been removed. The current $\dot{q}_n$ through the output impedance Z_n is then given by the simple relation

$$\dot{q}_n = V/(Z + Z_n).$$ (503.12)

Hence, the impedance Z plays the role of the series impedance of the generator as indicated in Fig. 5.11a, and V represents its voltage.

The proof for Thevenin's theorem will be carried out with the node analysis, so that the impedances Z_n and Z enter through the admittances $Y_n = Z_n^{-1}$ and $Y = Z^{-1}$. Consider the schematic diagram of a four-terminal network with an admittance Y_n connected across its output (Fig. 5.16). We have for the network equations of the four-terminal network itself, as in Fig. 5.15.

$$\begin{pmatrix} y_{11} & y_{12} \\ y_{21} & y_{22} \end{pmatrix} \begin{pmatrix} v_1 \\ v_2 \end{pmatrix} = \begin{pmatrix} \dot{q}_1 \\ \dot{q}_2 \end{pmatrix}.$$ (503.13)

If the admittance Y_n were included in the four-terminal network, then the output current would be $\dot{q}_2{}'$ (Fig. 5.16), which is related

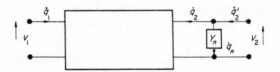

Fig. 5.16. Schematic diagram of a four-terminal network with an admittance Y_n connected across the output.

to the current through the admittance Y_n,

$$\dot{q}_n = Y_n v_2,$$ (503.14)

and to the current $\dot{q}_2$ in (503.13) by the following statement of Kirchhoff's current law

$$\dot{q}_2{}' - \dot{q}_n - \dot{q}_2 = 0.$$ (503.15)

By inserting (503.14) into (503.15), solving for $\dot{q}_2$ and substituting that expression in (503.13) and rearranging, one obtains the following equations for the four-terminal network whose boundaries have been extended to enclose the admittance Y_n.

$$\begin{pmatrix} y_{11} & y_{12} \\ y_{21} & (y_{22} + Y_n) \end{pmatrix} \begin{pmatrix} v_1 \\ v_2 \end{pmatrix} = \begin{pmatrix} \dot{q}_1 \\ \dot{q}_2{}' \end{pmatrix}. \tag{503.16}$$

There is a current source connected to the input, but none is connected to the output, so that $\dot{q}_2{}'$ vanishes, and for the case under consideration the network equations assume the form

$$\begin{pmatrix} y_{11} & y_{12} \\ y_{21} & (y_{22} + Y_n) \end{pmatrix} \begin{pmatrix} v_1 \\ v_2 \end{pmatrix} = \begin{pmatrix} \dot{q}_1 \\ 0 \end{pmatrix}. \tag{503.17}$$

The following relation between the output and input voltages comes immediately from (503.17):

$$v_2 = - \frac{y_{21}v_1}{y_{22} + Y_n}, \tag{503.18}$$

It follows from (503.14) and (503.18) that the current through the admittance Y_n may be written

$$\dot{q}_n = - \frac{y_{21}Y_n v_1}{y_{22} + Y_n}, \tag{503.19}$$

which may be rearranged to give the expression

$$\dot{q}_n = \left(- \frac{y_{21}v_1}{y_{22}} \right) \left\{ \frac{1}{y_{22}} + \frac{1}{Y_n} \right\}^{-1}, \tag{503.20}$$

or

$$\dot{q}_n = \left(- \frac{y_{21}v_1}{y_{22}} \right) \left\{ \frac{1}{y_{22}} + Z_n \right\}^{-1}. \tag{503.21}$$

It follows from (503.21) that if we can show that $-y_{21}v_1/y_{22}$ is the open circuit output voltage of the network, and $1/y_{22}$ is its source impedance, then we have obtained a proof of Thevenin's theorem.

When the ouput voltage of the system is determined with Y_n removed, then $\dot{q}_2$ vanishes in (503.13), and it follows that the open circuit output voltage is given by the expression

$$v_2 = -y_{21}v_1/y_{22}, \qquad (503.22)$$

which satisfies the first of the two requirements in the proof. It remains to show that y_{22}^{-1} equals the source impedance Z of the network. In order to determine the source impedance of the network, i.e., the impedance presented by the box (Fig. 5.15) to its output terminals, it is necessary to turn off the generator supplying v_1 (short-circuit the input making $v_1 = 0$), inject a current $\dot{q}_2$ into the output and determine the resulting voltage v_2. As $v_1 = 0$, we have

$$y_{22}v_2 = \dot{q}_2. \qquad (503.23)$$

Therefore, y_{22}^{-1} equals the source impedance Z of the network.
Q. E. D.

Theorems VII and IX together yield a corollary, commonly called Norton's theorem, which states that any network may be replaced by an equivalent current source.

Corollary III *(Norton's theorem)*: If an admittance Y_n is connected between two points of a network, the resulting voltage across this admittance is the ratio of the short circuit output current of the network to the sum of Y_n and Y the admittance of the network measured between the two points.

Let us apply Thevenin's Theorem to the simple circuit shown in Fig. 5.17a in order to determine the behavior of the capacitor C. According to Thevenin's theorem, the circuit in Fig. 5.17a may be replaced by the one in Fig. 5.17b as far as the behavior

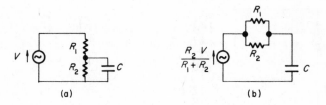

Fig. 5.17.   (a) Schematic circuit diagram. (b) Schematic diagram of a circuit in which the behavior of the capacitor C is the same as in (a) by Thevenin's theorem.

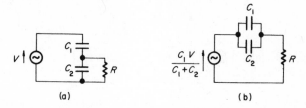

Fig. 5.18.   (a) Schematic circuit diagram. (b) Schematic diagram of a circuit in which the behavior of the resistor R is the same as in (a) by Thevenin's theorem.

of the capacitor C is concerned. As the two parallel resistors behave as one with the resistance $R_1 R_2 (R_1 + R_2)^{-1}$, it may be seen that the behavior of the capacitor is the same as if it were in a simple series RC circuit. As these remarks apply for all frequencies, it follows by Theorem IV (superposition) that they also apply to the transient solution. Hence, the RC time constant of the circuit in Fig. 5.17a is the same as that in Fig. 5.17b, viz., $R_1 R_2 C (R_1 + R_2)^{-1}$. By following essentially the same steps, one may apply Thevenin's theorem to the circuit in Fig. 5.18a to determine the behavior of the resistor R and show that it is the same as in the simple RC circuit shown in Fig. 5.18b.

Consider the typical bridge circuit shown in Fig. 5.19a. The behavior of the bridge is the same if the direct connection

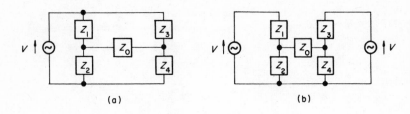

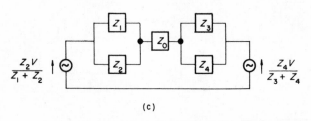

Fig. 5.19.   (a) Typical bridge circuit. (b) Diagram of a circuit equivalent to (a). (c) Schematic diagram of a circuit in which the behavior of the impedance Z_0 is the same as in (b) by Thevenin's theorem.

is removed between impedances Z_1 and Z_3, providing another generator is added to maintain all parts of the circuit at the same potential Fig. (5.19b). Hence, the behavior of the circuits shown in Figs. 5.19a and b is the same. By applying Thevenin's theorem to determine the behavior of the impedance Z_0, first at the connection between impedance Z_1 and Z_2, and then at the connection between the impedance Z_3 and Z_4, one obtains the equivalent circuit shown in Fig. 5.19c. It is evident, of course, that the bridge is balanced (no current flows through the impedance of the detector Z_0) if $Z_2(Z_1 + Z_2)^{-1} = Z_4(Z_3 + Z_4)^{-1}$, or $Z_1 Z_2^{-1} = Z_3 Z_4^{-1}$; the current through Z_0 gives the sensitivity of the bridge and this is merely the current through a simple series circuit.

The input and output of a four-terminal network may be interchanged by interchanging subscripts 1 and 2 in (503.13). Hence, by interchanging these subscripts in (503.16), and replacing Y_n by Y_1, we obtain the secular equations for the four-terminal network shown in Fig. 5.20, e.g.,

$$\begin{pmatrix} (y_{11} + Y_1) & y_{12} \\ y_{21} & y_{22} \end{pmatrix} \begin{pmatrix} v_1 \\ v_2 \end{pmatrix} = \begin{pmatrix} \dot{q}_1 \\ \dot{q}_2 \end{pmatrix}. \qquad (503.24)$$

It follows that the secular equations for the four-terminal network shown in Fig. 5.21 may be obtained by the same argument used to obtain (503.16) as an extension of (503.13). Therefore, the secular equations for the four-terminal network (Fig. 5.21) may be written

$$\begin{pmatrix} (y_{11} + Y_1) & y_{12} \\ y_{21} & (y_{22} + Y_2) \end{pmatrix} \begin{pmatrix} v_1 \\ v_2 \end{pmatrix} = \begin{pmatrix} \dot{q}_1 \\ \dot{q}_2 \end{pmatrix}. \qquad (503.25)$$

Consider a special type of four-terminal network in which there is a common connection between the input and the output

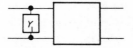

Fig. 5.20.   Schematic diagram of a four-terminal network with added shunt input admittance.

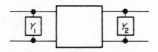

Fig. 5.21.   Schematic diagram of a four-terminal network with added shunt admittance at the input and output.

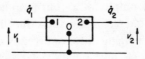

Fig. 5.22. Schematic diagram of a three-terminal network.

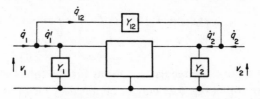

Fig. 5.23. Schematic diagram of a composite three-terminal network with a Π-network connected around a three-terminal network.

(Fig. 5.22). Vacuum tubes, transistors, and a certain class of filters may be represented by this schematic diagram (Fig. 5.22) which will be referred to as a three-terminal network. Figure 5.23 shows a three-terminal network with the input and the output coupled directly through the admittance Y_{12}. The secular equations for this reduced system may be written by inspection as follows

$$(y_{11} + Y_1)v_1 + y_{12}v_2 = \dot{q}_1{}' = \dot{q}_1 - \dot{q}_{12},$$
$$y_{21}v_1 + (y_{22} + Y_2)v_2 = \dot{q}_2{}' = \dot{q}_2 + \dot{q}_{12}. \tag{503.26}$$

The component of current fed from the input to the output through the admittance Y_{12} is given by the expression

$$\dot{q}_{12} = Y_{12}(v_1 - v_2). \tag{503.27}$$

By inserting (503.27) into (503.26), and rearranging, the secular equations may be written in the following matrix form

$$\begin{pmatrix} (y_{11} + Y_1 + Y_{12}) & (y_{12} - Y_{12}) \\ (y_{21} - Y_{12}) & (y_{22} + Y_2 + Y_{12}) \end{pmatrix} \begin{pmatrix} v_1 \\ v_2 \end{pmatrix} = \begin{pmatrix} \dot{q}_1 \\ \dot{q}_2 \end{pmatrix}. \tag{503.28}$$

It may be seen that the admittance matrix in (503.28) is the following matrix sum,

$$\begin{pmatrix} y_{11} & y_{12} \\ y_{21} & y_{22} \end{pmatrix} + \begin{pmatrix} (Y_1 + Y_{12}) & -Y_{12} \\ -Y_{12} & (Y_2 + Y_{12}) \end{pmatrix}. \qquad (503.29)$$

The matrix on the left-hand side is the admittance matrix (503.13) and refers to the blank box, and the elements in the matrix on the right refer only to the Π-network shown in Fig. 5.24, which is connected around the blank box in Fig. 5.23.

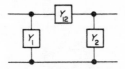

Fig. 5.24. Π-network.

One might expect the admittance matrix on the right-hand side to be that of the Π-network, which is indeed the case, as the matrix on the right-hand side in (503.29) may be obtained from Theorem VIII and Fig. 5.24 on inspection. Thus, we have proved a special case of the following theorem. The general proof which is simple has been left as an exercise.

Theorem X: The admittance matrix of a composite three-terminal network is the sum of the admittance matrices of the interconnected networks.

The utility of Theorem X may be illustrated by using it to obtain some of the relations under discussion. For example, Fig. 5.25a shows a special case of a Π network which has the admittance matrix

$$\begin{pmatrix} 0 & 0 \\ 0 & Y_2 \end{pmatrix}. \qquad (503.30)$$

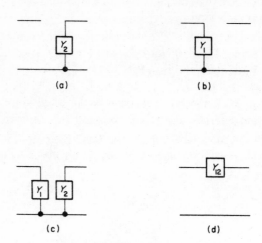

Fig. 5.25.   Special cases of a Π-network.

By letting Y_2 represent Y_n in Fig. 5.16, one may proceed from (503.13) directly to (503.16) by Theorem X. The special case of a Π-network shown in Fig. 5.25b has the admittance matrix

$$\begin{pmatrix} Y_1 & 0 \\ 0 & 0 \end{pmatrix}. \tag{503.31}$$

One may obtain (503.24) directly from (503.13) by Theorem X. The special case of a Π-network shown in Fig. 5.25c is a composite three-terminal network obtained by interconnecting the networks shown in Figs. 5.25a and b, and therefore, its admittance matrix is the sum of (502.30) and (503.31) by Theorem X, i.e., the circuit in Fig. 5.25c has the admittance matrix

$$\begin{pmatrix} Y_1 & 0 \\ 0 & Y_2 \end{pmatrix}. \tag{503.32}$$

It may be seen that the admittance matrix of the circuit shown in Fig. 5.21 may be obtained at once from (503.13) and (503.32) by Theorem X to obtain the admittance matrix in (503.25). Standing alone, the networks shown in Figs. 5.25a, b, and c are trivial, because there is no interaction between the input and the output, and the only point in considering them as Π-networks is that one may use Theorem X to conveniently account for their incorporation into a three-terminal network. A special case of a network in which the input interacts with the output is shown in Fig. 5.25d. In this case the input current is given by (503.27) and the output current is -1 times the input current. Therefore, the network (Fig. 5.25d) has the admittance matrix

$$\begin{pmatrix} Y_{12} & -Y_{12} \\ -Y_{12} & Y_{12} \end{pmatrix}. \tag{503.33}$$

The Π-network (Fig. 5.24) may be regarded as a composite three-terminal network obtained by combining the networks shown in Figs. 5.25c and d. Therefore, it follows by Theorem X that one may add the admittance matrices (503.32) and (503.33) to obtain the admittance matrix of the Π-network

$$\begin{pmatrix} (Y_1 + Y_{12}) & -Y_{12} \\ -Y_{12} & (Y_2 + Y_{12}) \end{pmatrix}. \tag{503.34}$$

Finally, the admittance matrix of the circuit shown in Fig. 5.23, which is contained in (503.28), may be obtained directly from Theorem X using (503.13) and (505.34).

5.0.4. Gyrators

We now consider several physical systems which have the common property that the Lagrangian in each case contains a *gyroscopic term*, i.e., a term which is linear in the velocity. In each example, the gyroscopic term enters through the presence in the system of a static magnetic field. As charge carriers move through the static magnetic field, they are subject to the force $q\dot{\mathbf{r}} \times \mathbf{B}$ with q the electronic charge, $\dot{\mathbf{r}}$ the drift velocity and $\mathbf{B}$ the magnetic induction (Heaviside, 1889; Lorentz, 1892), and it is this force that gives rise to the gyroscopic term in the Lagrangian.

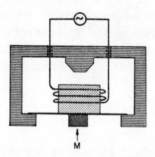

Fig. 5.26. Schematic diagram of a permanent magnet loudspeaker.

The permanent magnet loudspeaker (Fig. 5.26) is a simple example of a gyrator. The speaker cone is represented simply as a diaphragm stretched across the mouth of the permanent magnet. The diaphragm is loaded in the center with a mass M which represents the combined mass of the coil, cone, and the air moved by the motion of the cone. The coil is constrained so that it may move only along its axis, and we let x represent the displacement of the coil from its equilibrium position. The magnetic flux linked by the coil varies with x. Only small displacements are considered so that the flux linked by the coil may be expressed by the first-order approximation

$$g(x) = g_0 + g'x. \tag{504.1}$$

There are two coordinates of interest, x the linear displacement of the mass, and q a cyclic coordinate which enters only in the current $\dot{q}$ through the coil. The coil is considered to have an inductance L and a resistance R, and the generator applies a voltage $V(t)$ to the coil. As $\dot{q}$, the current through the coil, links the magnetic flux $g(x)$, there is a kinetic energy term $\dot{q}g(x)$ which must appear in the conservative part of the Lagrangian, and this contributes a gyroscopic term. The conservative part of the Lagrangian may be written

$$\mathscr{L}' = \tfrac{1}{2} L\dot{q}^2 + \tfrac{1}{2} M\dot{x}^2 + \dot{q}g(x) - \tfrac{1}{2} Ux^2, \qquad (504.2)$$

in which $\tfrac{1}{2} Ux^2$ is the potential energy associated with the stiffness of the diaphragm. By referring to Postulate IIa, one finds that the dissipative Lagrangian term for the system may be written

$$\mathscr{L}'' = \tfrac{1}{2} R\dot{q}^2 + \tfrac{1}{2} R'\dot{x}^2, \qquad (504.3)$$

in which R' represents the viscous damping resistance produced by the motion of the speaker diaphragm. From the complete Lagrangian based on (504.2) and (504.3), one obtains the following equations of motion:

$$\left(\begin{bmatrix} L\dfrac{d}{dt} + R \end{bmatrix} \qquad g' \\ -g' \qquad \begin{bmatrix} M\dfrac{d}{dt} + R' + U\left(\dfrac{d}{dt}\right)^{-1} \end{bmatrix}\right)\begin{pmatrix} \dot{q} \\ \dot{x} \end{pmatrix} = \begin{pmatrix} V(t) \\ 0 \end{pmatrix}.$$

$$(504.4)$$

From (504.4), we see that a force $g'\dot{q}$ is applied to the mass M, and that the voltage applied by the generator is opposed by an induced voltage of magnitude $g'\dot{x}$. A common property of this gyrator and the others discussed here is illustrated by relation (504.4), viz., the secular matrix in each case contains gyroscopic terms of the kind discussed in connection with (500.6). In the case of (504.4) we have the antisymmetric coefficients $G_{12} = -G_{21} = g'$.

Consider the ideal case of a conservative system with the Lagrangian given only by the term (504.2). Such a conservative system has the equations of motion

$$\begin{pmatrix} L\dfrac{d}{dt} & g' \\ -g' & \left(M\dfrac{d}{dt} + U\left(\dfrac{d}{dt}\right)^{-1}\right) \end{pmatrix} \begin{pmatrix} \dot{q} \\ \dot{x} \end{pmatrix} = \begin{pmatrix} 0 \\ 0 \end{pmatrix}. \qquad (504.5)$$

which reduce to the following equation for an oscillator.

$$\left[M\frac{d^2}{dt^2} + U + \frac{(g')^2}{L}\right]\dot{x} = 0. \qquad (504.6)$$

The equation of simple harmonic motion (504.6) shows that the motion of the short circuited coil in the inhomogeneous field contributes an added stiffness to the diaphragm making the total force per unit displacement $U + (g')^2/L$, whereas it would be just U if the coil were open circuited.

With the generator supplying an ac voltage $V_0 e^{i\omega t}$, the equations of motion have the form

$$\begin{pmatrix} i\omega L + R & g' \\ -g' & \left(i\omega M + R' + \dfrac{U}{i\omega}\right) \end{pmatrix} \begin{pmatrix} \dot{q} \\ \dot{x} \end{pmatrix} = \begin{pmatrix} V_0 e^{i\omega t} \\ 0 \end{pmatrix}, \qquad (504.7)$$

Solving for the current, one finds that the impedance presented by the system to the generator is given by

$$Z = i\omega L + R + \frac{(g')^2}{R' + i\omega M + (U/i\omega)}. \qquad (504.8)$$

Equation (504.8) shows that the inertial effect of the mass, and the stiffness and damping of the diaphragm, are the same as if the parallel circuit in Fig. 5.27 were connected in series with the

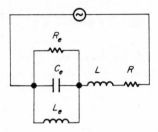

Fig. 5.27. Equivalent electrical circuit of a permanent magnet loud-speaker. $(g')^2 = R'R_e = UL_e = M/C_e$.

coil, as far as the electrical impedance of the system is concerned. The parallel circuit in Fig. 5.27 has an inductance $(g')^2/U$, a resistance $(g')^2/R'$, and a capacitance $M/(g')^2$. Similar electrical network analogies have been used extensively in the treatment of acoustical and mechanical systems by Olson (1943, 1947).

For small angular deflections, the D'Arsonval galvanometer may be classed as a gyrator. Its Lagrangian terms and equations of motion are similar to those of the permanent magnet loud-speaker. The linear displacement x of the coil in the loudspeaker is replaced by the angular displacement θ of the coil in the galvanometer, and the mass M of the moving parts of the loud-speaker is replaced by the moment of inertia I of the moving parts in the galvanometer. Where U stands for the force per unit displacement of the diaphragm, U gives the restoring torque per unit angular deflection of the spring in the galvanometer, and where R' is the viscous damping force per unit linear velocity with the loudspeaker, R' gives the viscous damping torque per unit angular velocity with the galvanometer. With no deflection, no magnetic flux links the coil, and for small deflections the flux linked by the coil may be written $g_1\theta$. Hence, we have for the conservative part of the Lagrangian

$$\mathscr{L}' = \tfrac{1}{2}L\dot{q}^2 + \tfrac{1}{2}I\dot{\theta}^2 + \dot{q}g(\theta) - \tfrac{1}{2}U\theta^2, \qquad (504.9)$$

and for the dissipative term

$$\mathscr{L}'' = \tfrac{1}{2} R \dot{q}^2 + \tfrac{1}{2} R' \dot{\theta}^2 . \qquad (504.10)$$

The complete Lagrangian based on (504.9) and (504.10) yields the equations of motion

$$\begin{bmatrix} \left(L\dfrac{d}{dt} + R \right) & g_1 \\[2ex] -g_1 & \left(I\dfrac{d}{dt} + R' + U\left(\dfrac{d}{dt}\right)^{-1} \right) \end{bmatrix} \begin{pmatrix} \dot{q} \\ \dot{\theta} \end{pmatrix} = \begin{pmatrix} V(t) \\ 0 \end{pmatrix}, \qquad (504.11)$$

which are very similar to those for the loudspeaker (504.4) and therefore the solutions are essentially the same except for obvious substitutions.

Direct current motors with either permanent magnets or shunt wound magnets are gyrators, and so are dc generators with permanent or shunt wound magnets. There is a small angular displacement between successive coils on the armature, so that only a small rotation of the armature is required to make the total flux linking the coils return to the same value. The total flux may be written $g(\theta) = g_0 + g_1\theta$, and through the switching of the coils by the commutator, $\dot{q}(\theta)$ with constant θ is maintained as a constant with a superimposed "ripple." As neither motors nor generators have a restoring spring, U vanishes in (504.11), but otherwise the conservative and dissipative terms in the Lagrangian are the same as for the galvanometer. Therefore, we have the equations of motion

$$\begin{bmatrix} \left(L\dfrac{d}{dt} + R \right) & g_1 \\[2ex] -g_1 & \left(I\dfrac{d}{dt} + R' \right) \end{bmatrix} \begin{pmatrix} \dot{q} \\ \dot{\theta} \end{pmatrix} = \begin{pmatrix} V(t) \\ K(t) \end{pmatrix}. \qquad (504.12)$$

If the torque $K(t)$ vanishes, then (504.12) represents a motor, and if the voltage $V(t)$ vanishes instead, then (504.12) represents a generator. Commencing with the equations of motion as the starting point, Kron (1935, 1959) has developed a general treatment for all classes of rotating electrical machines.

There is a solid state electronic device called the *Hall effect gyrator* (Mason *et al.* 1953; Wick, 1954). A schematic diagram is shown in Fig. 5.28. The cross hatched surface *s* forms a plane

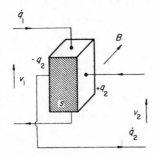

Fig. 5.28. Schematic diagram of a Hall effect gyrator.

perpendicular to the magnetic induction **B**, and all components of current in the semiconductor flow at right angles to the magnetic induction **B**. The input current is designated $\dot{q}_1$, and the deflection of the flowing charge $\dot{q}_1$ in the magnetic field produces a space charge $+q_2$ and $-q_2$ on opposite sides of the semiconducting sample. If the output is open circuited ($\dot{q}_2 = 0$), the charges $+q_2$ and $-q_2$ produce a transverse electric field which integrated across the sample from one output terminal to the other gives the Hall voltage

$$v_2 = R_{21}\dot{q}_1, \qquad \dot{q}_2 = 0, \qquad (504.13)$$

with

$$R_{21} = g/\mathscr{Q}, \qquad (504.14)$$

in which

$$\mathscr{Q} = b_{12}Nq, \qquad (504.15)$$

and
$$g = |\mathbf{B}| s. \tag{504.16}$$

The factor $\mathscr{Q}$ gives the effective number of charge carriers in the sample multiplied by the electronic charge $q, ..., N$ denoting the total number of charge carriers, and b_{12} is a dimensionless constant of the order unity which depends on the velocity distribution of the charge carriers. The factor g gives the total magnetic flux through the semiconductor. On the other hand, if the input is open circuited, and current is fed into the output, then the Hall voltage appears across the input, e.g.,

$$v_1 = - R_{21}\dot{q}_2, \qquad \dot{q}_1 = 0. \tag{504.17}$$

Just as the energy stored in a capacitor is $\frac{1}{2}qV$, the potential energy due to the separation of the charge is simply the product of the Hall voltage $R_{21}\dot{q}_1$, and the charge q_2, plus half the product $- R_{21}\dot{q}_2 q_1$. Thus, the conservative part of the Lagrangian may be written

$$\mathscr{L}' = - \tfrac{1}{2}R_{21}\dot{q}_1 q_2 + \tfrac{1}{2}R_{21}q_1\dot{q}_2. \tag{504.18}$$

It follows from Postulate IIa that the Hall effect gyrator has a dissipative Lagrangian term of the following form,

$$\mathscr{L}'' = \tfrac{1}{2} R_{11}\dot{q}_1{}^2 + \tfrac{1}{2} R_{22}\dot{q}_2{}^2, \tag{504.19}$$

in which R_{11} is the input resistance measured with $\dot{q}_2 = 0$, and R_{22} is the output resistance measured with $\dot{q}_1 = 0$. The Lagrangian terms (504.18) and (504.19) together yield the equations of motion

$$\begin{pmatrix} R_{11} & - R_{21} \\ R_{21} & R_{22} \end{pmatrix} \begin{pmatrix} \dot{q}_1 \\ \dot{q}_2 \end{pmatrix} = \begin{pmatrix} v_1 \\ v_2 \end{pmatrix}. \tag{504.20}$$

As the secular matrix in (504.20) is not symmetric, the reciprocity theorem does not hold. In fact, one of the important applications of the Hall effect gyrator utilizes a complete nullifi-

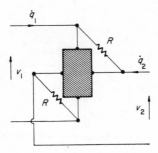

Fig. 5.29.   Isolating network.

cation of the reciprocity relation. For example, if the resistance R in Fig. 5.29 satisfies the following relation

$$R = (R_{11}R_{22} + R_{21}^2)/2R_{21}, \qquad (504.21)$$

then the input may interact with the output, but not vice versa.

The application of Theorem II to $\mathscr{L}'$ the conservative part of the Lagrangian, with the loudspeaker (504.2), the galvanometer, the motor or generator (504.9) gives a statement of the conservation of energy. However, with the Hall effect gyrator, Theorem II applied to (504.18) yields merely zero as its constant.

The behavior of the circuit shown in Fig. 5.29 may be treated conveniently by making the voltages serve as the independent variables. Hence, instead of (504.20), one has the secular equation

$$\begin{pmatrix} G_{11} & G_{12} \\ G_{21} & G_{22} \end{pmatrix} \begin{pmatrix} v_1 \\ v_2 \end{pmatrix} = \begin{pmatrix} \dot{q}_1 \\ \dot{q}_2 \end{pmatrix}, \qquad (504.22)$$

with

$$G_{11} = R_{22}/|R|, \qquad G_{22} = R_{11}/|R|$$
$$G_{12} = -G_{12} = R_{21}/|R|, \qquad |R| = R_{11}R_{22} + R_{21}^2 \qquad (504.23)$$

Consider the four-terminal network shown in Fig. 5.30 in which

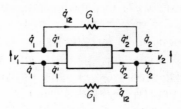

Fig. 5.30.   A composite four-terminal network.

both the corresponding input and output terminals are coupled through a conductance G_1. By applying Kirchhoff's current law at each of the tie points in Fig. 5.30, one obtains the following relations

$$\dot{q}_1' = \dot{q}_1 - \dot{q}_{12}, \quad \dot{q}_2' = \dot{q}_2 + \dot{q}_{12}. \qquad (504.24)$$

By following a path across the input, across the upper conductor, down across the output, and across the lower conductor, one may obtain the following relation by Kirchhoff's voltage law.

$$v_1 - \frac{\dot{q}_{12}}{G_1} - v_2 - \frac{\dot{q}_{12}}{G_1} = 0. \qquad (504.25)$$

Solving for the current $\dot{q}_{12}$, we have

$$\dot{q}_{12} = G_1(v_1 - v_2)/2. \qquad (504.26)$$

By inserting (504.24) and (504.26) into (504.22), we have

$$\begin{aligned}
G_{11}v_1 + G_{12}v_2 &= \dot{q}_1' = \dot{q}_1 - G_1(v_1 - v_2)/2, \\
G_{21}v_1 + G_{22}v_2 &= \dot{q}_2' = \dot{q}_2 + G_1(v_1 - v_2)/2,
\end{aligned} \qquad (504.27)$$

which may be rearranged and rewritten in the following matrix form

$$\begin{pmatrix} (G_{11} + G_1/2) & (G_{12} - G_1/2) \\ (G_{21} - G_1/2) & (G_{22} + G_1/2) \end{pmatrix} \begin{pmatrix} v_1 \\ v_2 \end{pmatrix} = \begin{pmatrix} \dot{q}_1 \\ \dot{q}_2 \end{pmatrix}. \qquad (504.28)$$

It follows from (504.23) and (504.28) that if the resistance R in Fig. 5.29 satisfies (504.21), then the input may interact with the output, but not vice versa.

It should be pointed out that although we have regarded the magnetic flux as a constant parameter, some practical applications of the Hall effect gyrator employ a magnetic flux which varies with the time (Weiss, 1956; 1964).

The following example concerns the electronic cyclotron frequency of solids as treated classically by the Drude model (see Section 5.0).

In treating cyclotron resonance, we take the effective displacement of the typical valence electron as a radius vector with two orthogonal coordinates, e.g.,

$$\mathbf{r} = \begin{pmatrix} y_1 \\ y_2 \\ 0 \end{pmatrix}. \tag{504.29}$$

The test specimen is placed in a dc magnetic field pointing in the direction of the third orthogonal coordinate, so that we have for the magnetic induction

$$\mathbf{B} = \begin{pmatrix} 0 \\ 0 \\ B \end{pmatrix}. \tag{504.30}$$

Thus, we have for the corresponding magnetic vector potential

$$\mathbf{A} = \tfrac{1}{2} B \begin{pmatrix} -y_2 \\ y_1 \\ 0 \end{pmatrix}. \tag{504.31}$$

As the typical electron has the kinetic energy,

$$T = \tfrac{1}{2} m \,|\,\dot{\mathbf{r}}\,|^2, \tag{504.32}$$

and the potential energy,

$$U = q\dot{\mathbf{r}} \cdot \mathbf{A}, \tag{504.33}$$

the conservative part of the Lagrangian may be written,

$$\mathcal{L}' = \tfrac{1}{2} m\dot{y}_1^{\,2} + \tfrac{1}{2} m\dot{y}_2^{\,2} + \tfrac{1}{2} qB\dot{y}_1 y_2 - \tfrac{1}{2} qBy_1 \dot{y}_2, \qquad (504.34)$$

in which there are two gyroscopic terms in which the coefficients introduced earlier Section (5.0) as G_{sj} take the form $G_{12} = qB = -G_{21}$.

The well-known cyclotron resonance frequency

$$\omega_0 = qB/m \qquad (504.35)$$

has a wavelength of 2.1 mm with a magnetic field of 50 kg. Hence, with the greatest magnetic fields obtainable in the laboratory, the resonant frequency is so small that radiation damping losses are negligible compared with electronic scattering by phonons and by impurities. Thus, in the nonconservative part of the Lagrangian, it is necessary to take into account only the dissipation function, viz.,

$$\mathcal{L}'' = \frac{m}{2\tau} \dot{y}_1^{\,2} + \frac{m}{2\tau} \dot{y}_2^{\,2}. \qquad (504.36)$$

As an external force, a circularly polarized ac electric field is introduced,

$$\mathbf{J} = \begin{pmatrix} -1 \\ i \\ 0 \end{pmatrix} qE_0 e^{i\omega t}. \qquad (504.37)$$

It follows by (500.5) (504.34), and (504.36) that the system has the following equations of motion.

$$\ddot{y}_1 + \frac{\dot{y}_1}{\tau} + \omega_0 \dot{y}_2 = -qE_0 e^{i\omega t}/m, \qquad (504.38)$$

$$-\omega_0 \dot{y}_1 + \ddot{y}_2 + (\dot{y}_2/\tau) = iqE_0 e^{i\omega t}/m. \qquad (504.39)$$

The steady state solution of (504.38) and (504.39) may be

written

$$\dot{y}_1 = -\frac{q\tau E_0 e^{i\omega t}}{m\left[1 + i(\omega - \omega_0)\tau\right]} = i\dot{y}_2.$$ (504.40)

In order to obtain the mean power dissipated per electron, we evaluate the real part of the *complex power*, e.g.,

$$\frac{2}{t_2 - t_1}\int_{t_1}^{t_2} \mathscr{L}'' \, dt = \text{Re}\,\tfrac{1}{2}\left[J_1^*\dot{y}_1 + J_2^*\dot{y}_2\right]$$

$$= \frac{q^2\tau E_0^2}{m\left[1 + (\omega - \omega_0)^2\tau^2\right]}.$$ (504.41)

It may be seen by (504.41) that the maximum rate of energy loss occurs when the frequency equals ω_0 and that the resonance is sharply defined if $\omega_0\tau \gg 1$.

5.0.5. Harmonic Modes

At first it might seem from the appearance of the equations of motion (500.6) that only the electric dipole loss could be accounted for. A few remarks are added in this section to show that the losses from other modes are not excluded.

Consider the simple electromagnetic system illustrated in Fig. 5.1. The system is unshielded, and therefore it is coupled to its surroundings through stray capacitance and mutual inductance. If we were able to account for all these electromagnetic couplings and write the proper impedance matrix for the system, it would be of high order, and the secular equation would take the general form

$$\sum_{s=0}^{n} A_s \frac{d^s}{dt^s} q = 0,$$ (505.1)

with n a large number. The predominant coefficients in the series (505.1) are $A_3 = -P$ for the electric dipole radiation damping,

$A_2 = L_0$ the self inductance, $A_1 = R$ the resistance associated with relaxation losses, and $A_0 = 1/C$ giving the reciprocal of the capacitance. One may see that the coefficients A_s vanish with S odd in conservative systems.[†] Ordinarily $A_1 = R$ predominates in the coefficients A_s with S odd, $A_3 = -P$ being usually much smaller. The coefficient A_5, which could be expected to be appreciably smaller than A_3, accounts for both the magnetic dipole and electric quadrupole radiation losses. Although the coefficients A_s with $S > 3$ are small, they provide additional roots in the solution of the secular polynomial (505.1), so that the oscillator has not only the fundamental frequency, but also harmonic frequencies entering into its normal modes. Hence, by considering the coupling of the circuit (Figure 5.1) with its surroundings, we are forced to consider both the higher modes of vibration and higher modes of radiation.

Consider the somewhat more complicated electromagnetic system illustrated by Fig. 5.2, which also is unshielded from its surroundings, and therefore may interact with them through stray capacitance and mutual inductance. Again, the secular equation of the system may be represented by (505.1), but the predominant coefficients A_s are those with $S < 7$. The interrelation between the normal modes of this system would be, of course, more complicated than with the previous case, and the coefficient A_5, which accounts for the magnetic dipole and electric quadrupole radiation, would be much more pronounced.

5.0.6. Motion of a Rigid Body with Damping

The treatment of rigid bodies in Section 4.0.1 is extended here to account for viscous damping through air resistance. Consider

---

[†] Systems of the kind illustrated by Fig. 5.1 and 5.2 do not have gyroscopic terms in $\mathscr{L}'$. However, with gyroscopic terms present we may have coefficients A_s in odd terms that do not dissipate energy, e.g., see Sections 5.0.1 and 5.0.4.

a free unconstrained rigid body. The conservative part of the Lagrangian is given by the kinetic energy term in (401.37), e.g.,

$$\mathscr{L}' = \tfrac{1}{2}\left[I_1\dot\varepsilon_1{}^2 + I_2\dot\varepsilon_2{}^2 + I_3\dot\varepsilon_3{}^2\right]. \tag{506.1}$$

Similarly, the nonconservative part of the Lagrangian takes the following form of the dissipation function,

$$\mathscr{L}'' = \tfrac{1}{2}\left[(I_1/\tau_1)\dot\varepsilon_1{}^2 + (I_2/\tau_2)\dot\varepsilon_2{}^2 + (I_3/\tau_3)\dot\varepsilon_3{}^2\right], \tag{506.2}$$

in which τ_1, τ_2, and τ_3 represent the relaxation times for each of the three principal axes respectively. It follows from (500.5) and the arguments used to obtain Euler's equations of motion for a free rigid body (401.44), (401.45), and (401.46), that with damping, those equations take the following form.

$$I_3\ddot\varepsilon_3 + (I_3/\tau_3)\dot\varepsilon_3 - (I_1 - I_2)\dot\varepsilon_1\dot\varepsilon_2 = 0, \tag{506.3}$$

$$I_1\ddot\varepsilon_1 + (I_1/\tau_1)\dot\varepsilon_1 - (I_2 - I_3)\dot\varepsilon_2\dot\varepsilon_3 = 0, \tag{506.4}$$

$$I_2\ddot\varepsilon_2 + (I_2/\tau_2)\dot\varepsilon_2 - (I_3 - I_1)\dot\varepsilon_3\dot\varepsilon_1 = 0. \tag{506.5}$$

Now we consider the rotary motion of a disk, for which $I_1 = I_2$, and $\tau_1 = \tau_2$ through symmetry. It is easy to see that air resistance has a negligible effect on rotation about the axis of symmetry as compared with rotation about an axis in the equatorial plane, so that τ_3 is very much greater than $\tau_1 = \tau_2$. We will consider an interval of observation which is long compared with τ_1 but short compared with τ_3. Thus, the second term on the left-hand side in (506.3) may be neglected, and the third term vanishes by symmetry, so that the angular velocity about the axis of symmetry may be considered constant, and we have

$$\dot\varepsilon_3(t) = \text{const.} = \omega_3. \tag{401.47}$$

Thus, if we let

$$\omega_0 = \left(\frac{I_1 - I_3}{I_1}\right)\omega_3, \tag{401.48}$$

then (506.4) and (506.5) reduce to the matrix equation

$$\begin{bmatrix} \left(\dfrac{d}{dt} + \dfrac{1}{\tau_1}\right) & -\omega_0 \\[2mm] \omega_0 & \left(\dfrac{d}{dt} + \dfrac{1}{\tau_1}\right) \end{bmatrix} \begin{pmatrix} \dot{\varepsilon}_1 \\ \dot{\varepsilon}_2 \end{pmatrix} = \begin{pmatrix} 0 \\ 0 \end{pmatrix}. \qquad (506.6)$$

If we take for the boundary conditions

$$\dot{\varepsilon}_1(0) = 0, \qquad\qquad (401.50)$$

$$\dot{\varepsilon}_2(0) = \omega_1, \qquad\qquad (401.51)$$

we have the following solution

$$\dot{\varepsilon}_1(t) = \omega_1 e^{-t/\tau_1} \sin \omega_0 t, \qquad (506.7)$$

$$\dot{\varepsilon}_2(t) = \omega_1 e^{-t/\tau_1} \cos \omega_0 t. \qquad (506.8)$$

The above solution describes the motion of a disk spinning about its center of mass. The disk originally wobbles with its instantaneous axis of rotation precessing about the angular momentum as discussed in connection with the motion of a football (Chapter 4, Section 4.0.1). However, damping decreases the separation between the instantaneous axis of rotation and the angular momentum until they become colinear along the axis of symmetry.

A trick performed by jugglers is to maintain a number of plates spinning simultaneously each about its center on the end of a pointed rod. This trick, although difficult, is facilitated by the damping action treated here.

5.1. Active Systems

Taking the nonconservative physical systems considered thus far, their free motions in the absence of external forces exhibit an over-all attenuation with increasing time. Accordingly, the term *passive* is applied to these systems. On the other hand, the term *active* is applied to physical systems whose free motions can increase in amplitude with increasing time. For example, a passive electrical network may be combined with a transistor to form an active system. Similarly, an amplidyne generator, or a beam power pentode, may be connected to a passive electro-mechanical system to give an active system. It will have to suffice here merely to summarize the behavior of active systems. For detailed discussions, the following references are cited:

(a) Vacuum tubes: Spangenberg (1948), Dow (1952),
(b) Transistors: Shockley (1949), Ryder and Kircher (1949),
(c) Amplidynes: Kron (1959).

Transistors have three terminals and may be represented schematically by Fig. 5.22. The input current $\dot{q}_1(V_1, V_2)$ and output current $\dot{q}_2(V_1, V_2)$ are both functions of the input and output voltages V_1 and V_2. The transistor is usually connected through a passive electrical network to a dc power supply. Graphical methods are used to arrive at the appropriate external circuits and power supply voltage to give stable values of $\dot{q}_1$ and $\dot{q}_2$. As the transistor is to be used to amplify small signals for the most part, the behavior ordinarily depends on just the small amplitude fluctuations of $\dot{q}_1$ and $\dot{q}_2$, which may be analyzed by linear circuit theory. For example, taking the linear expansion

$$\begin{aligned}
d\dot{q}_1 &= \frac{\partial \dot{q}_1}{\partial V_1} dV_1 + \frac{\partial \dot{q}_1}{\partial V_2} dV_2, \\
d\dot{q}_2 &= \frac{\partial \dot{q}_2}{\partial V_1} dV_1 + \frac{\partial \dot{q}_2}{\partial V_2} dV_2,
\end{aligned} \tag{510.1}$$

one may analyze the differential variations in the conduction currents of a transistor by representing it as a three-terminal network obeying the following matrix equation

$$\begin{pmatrix} \dot{q}_1' \\ \dot{q}_2' \end{pmatrix} = \begin{pmatrix} g_{11} & g_{12} \\ g_{21} & g_{22} \end{pmatrix} \begin{pmatrix} V_1' \\ V_2' \end{pmatrix}, \tag{510.2}$$

in which $\dot{q}_i{}'$ and $V_i{}'$ stand for the differentials $d\dot{q}_i$ and dV_i, and the conductance elements g_{ij} represent the partial derivatives $\partial\dot{q}_i/\partial V_j$. Furthermore, the capacitance of the potential barriers and the capacitance between the connectors and the enclosure which encapsulates the transistor combine to form a Π-network as shown in Fig. 5.31. It follows by the argument used in con-

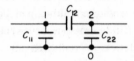

Fig. 5.31.   A Π-network of capacitors.

nection with Figure 5.23 and relations (503.28) and (503.29) that the transistor has the following admittance matrix

$$\begin{pmatrix} y_{11} & y_{12} \\ y_{21} & y_{22} \end{pmatrix}$$

$$= \begin{pmatrix} [g_{11} + i\omega(C_{11} + C_{12})] & (g_{12} - i\omega C_{12}) \\ (g_{21} - i\omega C_{12}) & [g_{22} + i\omega(C_{22} + C_{12})] \end{pmatrix}. \quad (510.3)$$

Both the conductance elements g_{ij} and the capacitance elements C_{ij} are functions of the total bias voltages V_1 and V_2. Furthermore, with the most common type of transistors in which the behavior is dominated by minority carriers injected into the base, the time dependence of the flow of minority carriers makes both the conductance elements g_{ij} and the capacitance elements C_{ij} dependent on the frequency, so that we should always note that g_{ij} signifies $g_{ij}(\omega)$, and C_{ij} signifies $C_{ij}(\omega)$.

Linear systems with transistors may be treated by mathematical models presented in previous sections. The effect of each transistor is accounted for by treating it as a three-terminal network with an admittance matrix y_{ij} as indicated in (510.3). Thus, the transistor becomes merely another linear circuit component, except that its admittance matrix is in general asymmetric $(y_{12} \neq y_{21})$, so that the reciprocity theorem does not hold. Another consequence of the asymmetry of the admittance matrix y_{ij}, is that the transistor may become unstable and break into oscillations. Before considering the subject of stability, some salient points about vacuum tubes will be reviewed.

A vacuum tube triode is also a three-terminal device. Its input and output conduction currents may be treated by the three-terminal network (Fig. 5.22), and its small amplitude current fluctuations may be treated by the linear equations (510.2). As with the transistor, the conductance matrices are in general asymmetric $(g_{12} \neq g_{21})$, and the elements g_{ij} are functions of the total input and output voltages V_1 and V_2. Under the most common operating conditions, the conductance elements g_{11} and g_{12} effectively vanish. Interelectrode capacitance, which is essentially voltage independent, may be treated as a Π-network (Fig. 5.31). Thus, the triode has an ac admittance matrix of the general form (510.3). The transit time of electrons between cathode and plate makes the conductance and capacitance elements of (510.3) become frequency dependent at very high frequencies.

The vacuum tube pentode has five electrodes: cathode, control grid, screen, suppressor, and plate. The screen and the suppressor are held at a fixed potential with respect to the cathode, and therefore the potential of only two electrodes may fluctuate with respect to the others. Consequently, as far as the fluctuations in conduction and displacement currents are concerned, the pentode may be treated by Figures 5.22 and 5.31, as with the triode, and by Eqs. (510.2) and (510.3). Hence, the same general methods that are used with transistors may also be applied to analyze the behavior of electrical and electromechanical systems containing triodes and pentodes.

5.1.1. Feedback

The effect of the coupling between the output and input of a physical system is termed *feedback*. Feedback coupling may be introduced into a system deliberately to gain one or the other of two very different objectives, viz., either to make the system oscillate, or to improve its stability. Whether or not feedback coupling is deliberately introduced into a system, a certain amount exists which may occasionally make the system unstable. A familiar example is the acoustic feedback between the loudspeaker and microphone of a public address system. Who has not witnessed the howling of these systems, either spontaneously or under the stimulus of the speaker's voice? In this section we are concerned with systems in which feedback is used, not to make them oscillate, but rather for a variety of other purposes, e.g., to improve stability, to increase or decrease input impedance, to perform certain computing operations, etc.

Servomechanisms or *servos*, are electromechanical systems with feedback coupling between the input and output. Automatic control systems and analog computers are built around servos. As feedback inherently plays a double role, i.e., it may either increase stability or decrease it, and the proper application of feedback requires a knowledge of its stability criteria. The purpose of this section is to give a brief review of these criteria.

It is necessary to define the term *stable* as used customarily with feedback amplifiers and servos. The term *stable* as applied to these feedback systems always indicates that any oscillations are damped. More specifically, a system with feedback is considered stable if all terms contained in its Green's function are damped; it is considered unstable if its Green's function contains one or more terms which increase in amplitude with the time and without limit. In practical cases, the oscillations of an unstable system may saturate at a fixed level through nonlinearity which becomes more pronounced at large amplitudes. Of course, the interpretation of the term *stable* as applied to feedback systems and to conservative systems is inconsistent, e.g., the oscillatory motion of a conservative system is ordinarily said to be stable.

We designate $G(\zeta)$ as the transform of the Green's function for the response of the output coordinate to an impulse applied to the input and call it the *transfer function*; with amplifiers $G(\zeta)$ with $\zeta = i\omega$ is called the *ac gain*. The nature of the transfer function will now be considered.

The transfer function may be written in the following form,

$$G(\zeta) = \frac{p(\zeta)}{|s(\zeta)|} \qquad (511.1)$$

in which $|s(\zeta)|$ is the secular determinant of the system. The polynomial $p(\zeta)$ is of lower degree than $|s(\zeta)|$ as explained in connection with (210.62). It is assumed that the roots of the secular determinant are distinct, i.e., $|s(\zeta)| = \prod_{i=1}^{n}(\zeta - a_i)$, which is generally true in practical cases. Therefore, by (210.62) and (210.66)–(210.68), the transfer function $G(\zeta)$ may be expanded as

$$G(\zeta) = \sum_{i=1}^{n} \frac{A_i}{\zeta - a_i}. \qquad (511.2)$$

Thus, we conclude that a feedback system is stable if and only if the secular determinant $|s(\zeta)|$ is a polynomial all of whose roots have negative real parts.

If there were no interaction whatever between the input and the output of the system, the secular determinant would reduce simply to $s_{11}(\zeta)s_{22}(\zeta)$. The effect of feedback modifies the secular determinant so that it may be written

$$|s(\zeta)| = s_{11}(\zeta)s_{22}(\zeta)[1 + \beta(\zeta)G_0(\zeta)], \qquad (511.3)$$

in which $G_0(\zeta)$ is the transfer function without feedback and

$\beta(\zeta)$ is the fraction of the output which is fed to the input through
the feedback coupling. Relation (511.3) follows from the
standard treatment of feedback, according to which the effect
of feedback on the transfer function of the system is to change
it from $G_0(\zeta)$ to

$$G(\zeta) = \frac{G_0(\zeta)}{1 + \beta(\zeta) G_0(\zeta)}. \qquad (511.4)$$

Two particular advantages of feedback may be seen in (511.4),
e.g., if $|\beta(\zeta)_0 G(\zeta)| \gg |$, then the transfer function reduces to
$\beta(\zeta)^{-1}$ which may be made to depend only on the feedback network instead of the entire system. As the feedback network may
be composed of temperature-compensated passive elements, it is
indeed an advantage to be able to make the transfer function
depend almost entirely on that network. The improvement in
stability through feedback may be also seen in the ratio,

$$\frac{dG(\zeta)}{G(\zeta)} = \frac{1}{1 + \beta(\zeta) G_0(\zeta)} \frac{dG_0(\zeta)}{G_0(\zeta)}, \qquad (511.5)$$

which shows that the percentage variation in the gain has been
reduced by the same factor that has reduced the gain itself.

The first thorough analysis of the stability criteria of physical
systems was apparently made by Routh (1877, 1892), who obtained a set of criteria to determine whether or not the secular
determinant had roots with real parts which were positive. He
also indicated how Cauchy's rule for contour integration could
be used to show whether the secular determinant had roots with
positive real parts. The method of contour integration was
worked out independently later by Nyquist (1932), and his
formulation of the method, which has been applied widely with
feedback amplifiers and servos, will now be considered.

It may be seen by (511.3) that the transient solution without
feedback is given by the roots of $s_{11}(\zeta)s_{22}(\zeta) = 0$, and as it can
be assumed that the system is stable without feedback, it is

necessary to be concerned only with the roots of the equation,

$$1 + \beta(\zeta) G_0(\zeta) = 0. \qquad (511.6)$$

The term $\beta(\zeta) G_0(\zeta)$ in (511.6) is called the *feedback transfer function*; by removing the feedback connection, the feedback transfer function $\beta(\zeta) G_0(\zeta)$ with $\zeta = i\omega$ can be measured, and the locus of this function in the complex plane is called the *Nyquist diagram*. The Nyquist diagram reveals whether or not there is a root of (511.6) with a positive real part. Note that the object of the Nyquist diagram is not to obtain the roots of (511.6), but merely to answer the question: Is the system stable?

It is assumed that (511.6) is analytic throughout the $(\zeta = \alpha + i\omega)$-plane so that angles are preserved in mapping from the ζ-plane to the $(\beta(\zeta) G_0(\zeta))$-plane. With the feedback coupling removed, a steady state measurement of the fraction of the output $\beta(\zeta) G_0(\zeta)$ is made over the following range of the argument,

$$\alpha = 0, \quad 0 < \omega < \omega_{max}$$

with ω_{max} the frequency where the transfer function has become insignificant. A Nyquist diagram of a stable feedback system is illustrated in Fig. 5.32. With the argument in the range $\alpha = \alpha_1 > 0, \quad 0 < \omega < \omega_{max}$, the locus of the feedback transfer

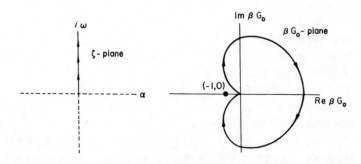

Fig. 5.32. Nyquist plot.

function appears as shown in Fig. 5.33. It is clear from Fig. 5.33 that $\beta(\zeta)G_0(\zeta)$ cannot be made to pass through the point $(-1,0)$, i.e., yield a root of $1 + \beta(\zeta)G_0(\zeta) = 0$ with ζ in the right half of the ζ-plane. A Nyquist diagram of an unstable feedback system is illustrated in Fig. 5.34 (solid line). It is apparent from Figure 5.34 that there is some positive value of α which will make $\beta(\zeta)G_0(\zeta)$ pass through the point $(-1, 0)$. Let this value

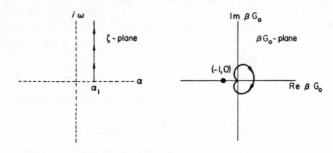

Fig. 5.33.   Plot of $\beta(i\omega)G_0(i\omega)$ with the argument increased by a positive real amount α_1.

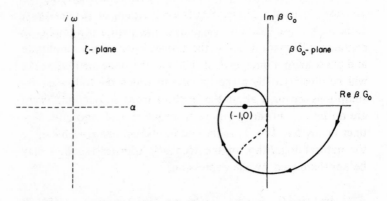

Fig. 5.34.   Nyquist plot of an unstable system (solid line). The dotted line shows how the plot might be modified if the system were stabilized by corrective engineering.

of α be denoted by α_4, and the frequency at which $\beta(\zeta)G_0(\zeta)$ passes through the point $(-1, 0)$ be denoted by ω_4. Then $1 + \beta(\zeta)G_0(\zeta) = 0$ has a root $\zeta = \alpha_4 + i\omega_4$ and consequently it must also have the root $\zeta = \alpha_4 - i\omega_4$. It follows that when the feedback connection is made, the system will oscillate at the angular frequency ω_4. In this case, as shown in Fig. 5.34, ω_4 occurs in the high frequency region of the system's spectrum. Any unstable system may be made stable by altering the phase-attenuation characteristics of $\beta(i\omega)G_0(i\omega)$ until the point $(-1, 0)$ is no longer enclosed with ω increasing, as indicated in Fig. 5.34 (dotted line).

Generalizing from the special cases illustrated by Figs. 5.32–5.34, we arrive at the following rule, called Nyquist's criterion: If the plot of $\beta(i\omega)G_0(i\omega)$ encircles the point $(-1, 0)$ with ω increasing, then the system is unstable; otherwise the system is stable.

A method of testing the stability of a system devised by Bode (1940, 1945) features a different way of plotting the feedback transfer function. The Bode diagrams show the logarithm of the feedback transfer function plotted against the logarithm of the frequency; the real part gives the amplitude in decibels and the imaginary part the phase. The Bode diagram of the real part alone may be used for a rough analysis of stability as it implicitly contains information about the phase, because the amplitude and phase are not independent. The way the Bode method works will be illustrated by a special case in which the following assumptions are made about the feedback transfer function: There are no zeros, and the poles are all negative, real, and quite distinct, i.e., $\alpha_1 \gg \alpha_2 \gg \alpha_3 \dots$. In the middle of the range $\alpha_m < \omega < \alpha_{m+1}$ the natural logarithm of the feedback transfer function may be approximated by the expression,

$$\ln \beta(i\omega) G_0(i\omega) \approx -m(\ln \omega + \tfrac{1}{2}i\pi) + \text{const.}, \qquad (511.7)$$

which is characterized by a constant slope in the amplitude with a constant phase. Converting the real part of (511.7) to decibels, e.g., rewriting (511.7) as follows

$$20 \log_{10} |\beta(i\omega) G_0(i\omega)| \approx -20m \log_{10} \omega, \qquad (511.8)$$

shows that the slope of the amplitude amounts to $6m$ dB/octave.[†] It may be inferred from (511.7) that the phase changes only where the slope of the amplitude changes, and from (511.7) and (511.8) together that a slope of η dB/octave gives a phase shift of roughly

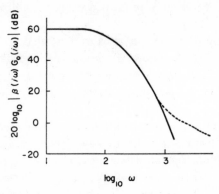

Fig. 5.35.   Bode plot corresponding to Fig. 5.34.

$\eta\pi/12$ rad. Thus, one may measure the amplitude of $\beta(i\omega) G_0(i\omega)$, without bothering about the phase, plot the Bode amplitude diagram, and from it visualize the corresponding Nyquist diagram. Ordinarily, instability can be expected where the feedback transfer function is unity and the phase equals or exceeds π. Thus, if the Bode diagram has a slope of 12 dB/octave or greater in the region of 0 dB, the system is unstable. Figure 5.35 shows the Bode diagram corresponding to the Nyquist diagram in Fig. 5.34.

[†] Let $\omega = 2^n\omega_f \approx 10^{0.3n}\omega_f$, with n the number of octaves over an arbitrary fundamental ω_f. Then a factor in gain ω^{-1}, e.g., $-20 \log_{10} \omega \approx -6n -20 \log_{10} \omega_f$ in dB, has a slope of ≈ -6 dB/octave.

Most amplifiers and servos are intended to have a constant transfer function over a given frequency range, and for this it is not enough if $\beta(i\omega)G_0(i\omega)$ merely satisfies the Nyquist stability criterion. For example, if the system is stable, but the locus of $\beta(i\omega)G_0(i\omega)$ even comes close to the point $(-1, 0)$, say in the narrow frequency range centered around ω_0, the transfer function will exhibit a maximum near ω_0. In order to make the locus of $\beta(i\omega)G_0(i\omega)$ maintain a satisfactory distance from the point $(-1, 0)$, the Bode diagram should have a slope of ~ 6 dB/octave in the region of 0 dB (see the dotted line portion of the corresponding Nyquist and Bode diagrams in Fig. 5.34 and 5.35).

A current method of examining the stability of a physical system employs a plot of poles and zeros in the ζ-plane. In this method the transfer function is written as follows.

$$\beta(\zeta)G_0(\zeta) = \frac{K_1 \prod_{j=1}^{m} (\zeta - b_j)}{\prod_{i=1}^{n} (\zeta - a_i)}. \tag{511.9}$$

The poles $\zeta_i = a_i$, and the zeros $\zeta_j = b_j$ of the feedback transfer function are plotted, together with the roots of (511.6) with the numerical factor K_1 varying over the range $0 < K_1 < \infty$. Any roots in the right-hand side half plane indicate that the system is unstable, while imaginary roots in the left-hand side half plane indicate that the system can undergo damped oscillations, and the damping factors and frequencies of oscillation are clearly indicated on the *root locus plot*.

Exercises

(5.1) Show that the locus of the impedance of the circuit (a) is a semicircle in the complex plane as indicated in (b), and that the locus of the admittance is also a semicircle in the complex plane as indicated in (c).

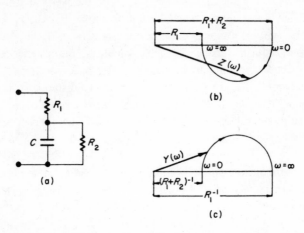

(5.2) Show that the locus of the impedance of the circuit (a) is a semicircle in the complex plane as indicated in (b), and that the locus of the admittance is also a semicircle in the complex plane as indicated in (c).

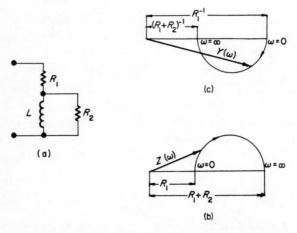

(5.3) Consider a mass with linear motion along a coordinate

x, elastically bound by a Hooke's law restoring force, subject to viscous damping, and driven by an external sinusoidal force

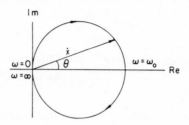

$J(t) = J_0 e^{i\omega t}$. For this simple system we may write the kinetic energy, the potential energy, and the dissipation function respectively as follows: $T = m\dot{x}^2/2$, $U = ux^2/2$, $F = \beta\dot{x}^2/2$.

(a) Show that

$$\beta\dot{x} = J_0 e^{i\omega t} \bigg/ \left[1 + iQ\left(\frac{\omega}{\omega_0} - \frac{\omega_0}{\omega}\right)\right]$$

with

$$\omega_0 = (u/m)^{\frac{1}{2}}, \quad \text{and} \quad Q = (mu)^{\frac{1}{2}}/\beta.$$

(b) Show that $Q = \omega_0/\Delta\omega$ with $\Delta\omega$ defining the frequency interval on either side of which the power $P(\omega)$ has the value $P_{max}/2$.

(c) Show that the locus of the velocity $\dot{x}$ is a circle in the complex plane (as indicated in the accompanying figure) with $\tan\theta = Q[(\omega/\omega_0) - (\omega_0/\omega)]$.

(5.4) Consider the motion of a damped harmonic oscillator after the application of an external force in the form of an impulse $J(t) = \delta(t)$. Except for the external force, the conditions are the same given for the previous problem.

(a) Show that with $Q > \frac{1}{2}$,

$$x(t) = \frac{\exp(-\beta t/2m)\sin\left[\omega_0 t(1 - (1/2Q)^2)^{\frac{1}{2}}\right]}{\left(mu[1 - (1/2Q)^2]\right)^{\frac{1}{2}}}.$$

(b) Show that with critical damping, i.e., $Q = \frac{1}{2}$,

$$x(t) = (t/m) \exp(-\beta t/2m).$$

(c) Show that with $Q < \frac{1}{2}$,

$$x(t) = \frac{\exp(-\beta t/2m) \sinh\left[(\beta t/2m)(1 - (2Q)^2)^{\frac{1}{2}}\right]}{\frac{1}{2}\beta(1 - (2Q)^2)^{\frac{1}{2}}}.$$

(5.5) Either a vacuum tube rectifier or a semiconductor diode is a two-terminal device which presents a very low impedance to a voltage of one polarity applied across its terminals, and a very high impedance to a voltage of the opposite polarity. The behavior of the filter circuit shown in the accompanying figure is practically the same as that of the circuit shown below. See Exercise 2.2.

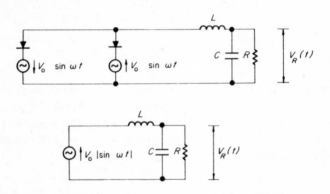

Show that the output voltage V_R may be written

$$V_R(t) = \frac{2V_0}{\pi}\left\{1 - 2\sum_{n=1}^{\infty}\frac{\cos(2n\omega t - \varphi_n)}{(4n^2 - 1)A(n\omega)}\right\},$$

with

$$\tan\varphi_n = \frac{2n\omega L}{R[1 - 4n^2\omega^2 LC]},$$

and

$$A(n\omega) = \left[(1 - 4n^2\omega^2 LC)^2 + \left(\frac{2n\omega L}{R} \right)^2 \right]^{\frac{1}{2}}$$

Hint: It is convenient to use Theorem IV (Superposition).

(5.6) Show that with a sinusoidal input voltage with constant amplitude, the amplitude of the output voltage is of the following form for each circuit shown in the accompanying figure.

$$V_1(\omega) = V_{1\max} \Bigg/ \left[1 + iQ \left(\frac{\omega}{\omega_0} - \frac{\omega_0}{\omega} \right) \right]$$

(a)

(b)

(c)

(d)

For circuits (a), (b), and (c), $Q = \frac{1}{3}$ and $\omega_0 = (CR)^{-1}$, and for circuit (d),

$$Q = \tfrac{1}{2}(1 - \kappa^2)^{\frac{1}{2}}, \quad \text{and} \quad \omega_0 = R/L\,(1 - \kappa^2)^{\frac{1}{2}}.$$

(5.7) Show that the small amplitude ac behavior of a pentode may be treated approximately by either one of the two equivalent circuits shown here. Hint: Refer to Theorems VII, and IX (Thevenin) and Eq. (510.2).

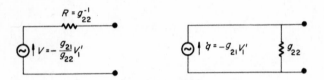

Equivalent voltage generator representation of a pentode. The meaning of the symbols is the same as in (510.2).

(5.8) Give arguments to support the use of the circuit shown here to represent the small amplitude behavior of a pentode amplifier with C_1, C_{12}, and C_2 representing the output capacitance of the pentode, the capacitance of the blocking capacitor, and the input capacitance of the next stage respectively.

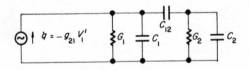

(5.9) Show that with $C_1 = C_2 = C_0 \ll C_{12}$, and $G_1 = G_2 = G$, the gain of the amplifier discussed in the previous problem is given by the expression

$$A(\omega) = A_{max} \bigg/ \left[1 + iQ\left(\frac{\omega}{\omega_0} - \frac{\omega_0}{\omega} \right) \right],$$

$$Q = (C_0/2C_{12})^{\frac{1}{2}}, \quad \text{and} \quad \omega_0 = G(2C_0 C_{12})^{-\frac{1}{2}}.$$

(5.10) Show that two identical cascaded amplifiers with gain as given in Exercise 5.9 cannot yield an unstable Nyquist diagram, whereas three identical cascade connected amplifiers can.

(5.11) Consider the twin-T-network shown in the accompanying figure. Show that the voltage V_4 vanishes for the frequency $\omega = G/C$, independent of the values of G_1 and G_4. Explain why the selectivity of the twin-T-network as a reject filter is best under the condition $G_1 \gg G \gg G_4$.

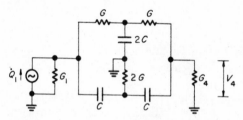

(5.12) Consider the twin-Π-network shown in the accompanying figure. Show that with $\omega = (RC)^{-1}$, the voltage drop across R_4 vanishes independent of the values of R_1 and R_4. Considering the voltage across R_4 as the output of this twin-Π-network, explain why its selectivity as a reject filter is best under the condition $R_1 \ll R \ll R_4$.

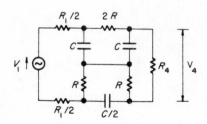

(5.13) Consider the behavior of the pulse transformer and associated circuitry shown here. The capacitance C has an initial charge $q(0)$ at time $t=0$, when the switch S is closed. Show that the output voltage $V_2(t)$ is given by the relation $(q(0)/C)\,(kN_2/N_1)e^{-Rt/L_1}$, $0 < t$, under the condition $(1/R)\,(L_1/C)^{\frac{1}{2}} \ll \frac{1}{2}$, with N_1 and N_2 the number of turns on the primary and secondary windings respectively, and κ the coupling coefficient.

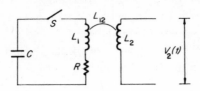

(5.14) Given that the total inductance is $L_1 + L_2 + 2L_{12}$ with a transformer connected as shown in the diagram.

Explain why the total inductance is changed to $L_1 + L_2 - 2L_{12}$ with the connections changed shown following.

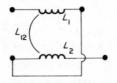

(5.15) The circuit shown here is a mutual inductance bridge, and when it is balanced, the induced current $\dot{q}_2$ vanishes. Show that the equations of motion may be written as

$$(L_1 + L_2 - 2L_{12})\ddot{q}_1 - (L_{13} - L_{23})\ddot{q}_2 = V(t),$$
$$-(L_{13} - L_{23})\ddot{q}_1 + L_3\ddot{q}_2 + R\dot{q}_2 = 0.$$

What conditions must be fulfilled to balance the bridge?

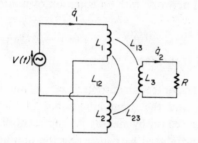

(5.16) Given that the three-terminal network connected as shown in (a) has the admittance matrix

$$\begin{pmatrix} y_{11} & y_{12} \\ y_{21} & y_{22} \end{pmatrix},$$

show that when the same network is connected as shown in (b), it has the admittance matrix

$$\begin{pmatrix} y_{11} & -(y_{11} + y_{12}) \\ -(y_{11} + y_{21}) & (y_{11} + y_{12} + y_{21} + y_{22}) \end{pmatrix},$$

and when connected as shown in (c), it has the admittance matrix

$$\begin{pmatrix} (y_{11} + y_{12} + y_{21} + y_{22}) & -(y_{12} + y_{22}) \\ -(y_{21} + y_{22}) & y_{22} \end{pmatrix}.$$

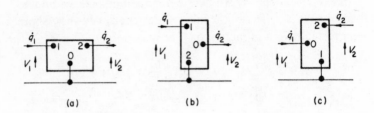

(a)   (b)   (c)

(5.17) Consider an amplifier which may be represented as a three-terminal network with an equation of motion,

$$\begin{pmatrix} y_{11} & 0 \\ y_{21} & y_{22} \end{pmatrix} \begin{pmatrix} v_1 \\ v_2 \end{pmatrix} = \begin{pmatrix} \dot{q}_0 \\ 0 \end{pmatrix} = \begin{pmatrix} y_0 v_0 \\ 0 \end{pmatrix}.$$

A current generator feeds a current $\dot{q}_0 = y_0 v_0$ into its own source admittance y_0 and the input admittance of the amplifier y_1, which is accounted for by making y_{11} represent the sum $y_0 + y_1$. Feedback is introduced by connecting the output to the input through an admittance y_{12} (see Fig. 5.23). The relative magnitudes of the admittances in the problem are indicated by the inequalities $y_{21} \gg y_{22} > y_{11} \gg y_{12}$. Show that the gain with feedback reduces to

$$\frac{v_2}{v_0} \approx -\frac{y_0 y_{21}/y_{11} y_{22}}{1 + (y_{12}/y_0)(y_0 y_{21}/y_{11} y_{22})}, \qquad \text{(therefore } \beta \approx y_{12}/y_0).$$

Show that the effect of feedback increases the input admittance by an amount $\sim y_{12} y_{21}/y_{22}$. Hint: It is convenient to use Theorem X.

CHAPTER 5 BIBLIOGRAPHY

BRILLOUIN, L. (1953). "Wave Propagation in Periodic Structures," 2nd ed. Dover, New York.

GUILLEMIN, E. A. (1953). "Introductory Circuit Theory." Wiley, New York.

LINDSAY, R. B. (1960). "Mechanical Radiation." McGraw-Hill, New York.

SOMMERFELD, A. (1952). "Electrodynamics." Academic Press, New York.
TWISS, R. Q. (1948). Linear-Circuit Analysis and Transient Response, *in* "Vacuum Tube Amplifiers" (G. E. Valley, Jr., and H. Wallman, eds.) Chap. 1. McGraw-Hill, New York.
WHITE, D. C., and WOODSON, H. H. (1959). "Electromechanical Energy Conversion." Wiley, New York.

CHAPTER 6

Lagrangian Density

*...you faithful solids and fluids; Through you color, form, location,
sublimity, ideality; Through you every proof, comparison, ...*

Walt Whitman—*Leaves of Grass*

6.0. Homogeneous Isotropic Media

The methods of analytical mechanics that have been presented
in the preceding chapters have not taken any special account of
such important features of the physical system as its uniformity,
isotropy, periodicity, etc. As these attributes dominate the
physical properties of such important systems as a single crystal,
a liquid, a gas, or even a vacuum, it is important to consider
how they enter into analytical mechanics, and that is the subject
of this chapter.

In principle, any system may be treated in terms of its
Lagrangian density. However, one profits by employing the
Lagrangian density only if the system has characteristic bulk
properties. For that reason, the following discussion under the
heading *Lagrangian Density* is limited to those systems which
display a characteristic Lagrangian density. Furthermore, where
it is clear from discussions in the preceding chapters that there
is a certain characteristic Lagrangian density, the treatment often
commences with the characteristic equations of motion that are
based on the Lagrangian density.

6.0.1. Poisson's Equation

Consider a homogeneous, isotropic, insulating medium with
permittivity ε, and charge density $q_v(\mathbf{r})$, which is a function of

position within the medium designated by the radius vector **r**. The system which is composed of this medium is of arbitrary shape and size, but it is entirely bounded by a conducting surface which is grounded and serves as the reference for designating the potential $V(\mathbf{r})$ within the system. It will be shown that this system may be represented by a symmetric network of capacitors connected in a cubic lattice with the external boundary of the network short circuited and connected to ground. For the time being, it will be assumed that the network has the same shape and the same size as the system under consideration.

The discussions in the previous chapter indicated that the standard treatment of electrical circuits may be derived from Hamilton's principle, and so we will start directly with the equations of motion. The network contains identical capacitors connected in a lattice with cubic symmetry, and because of this uniformity the equations of motion may be treated in terms of a typical branch of the total circuit (Fig. 6.1). The point in the

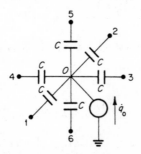

Fig. 6.1.   Typical branch of a periodic network with cubic symmetry.

diagram designated O represents any arbitrary point in the medium; it has a radius vector **r** with coordinates x_1, x_2, and x_3. That point is connected to one terminal of a current generator, the other terminal being connected to ground. The point O is also connected to its six nearest neighbors in the cubic lattice

TABLE 6.1

COORDINATES OF POINTS IN FIG. 6.1

Designation of point	Coordinates of point
0	(x_1, x_2, x_3)
1	$(x_1 + a, x_2, x_3)$
2	$(x_1 - a, x_2, x_3)$
3	$(x_1, x_2 + a, x_3)$
4	$(x_1, x_2 - a, x_3)$
5	$(x_1, x_2, x_3 + a)$
6	$(x_1, x_2, x_3 - a)$

through identical capacitors each with capacitance C. The coordinates of the neighboring points are designated in Table 6.1. The minimum separation between points in the lattice is the distance a, i.e., a is the lattice constant. Figure 6.1 represents every interior point of the system. Let us expand the potential to the second order for each point surrounding the central point in Fig. 6.1.

$$
\begin{aligned}
V_1 &= V_0 + (\partial V/\partial x_1)_0 a + \tfrac{1}{2}(\partial^2 V/\partial x_1{}^2)_0 a^2 , \\
V_2 &= V_0 - (\partial V/\partial x_1)_0 a + \tfrac{1}{2}(\partial^2 V/\partial x_1{}^2)_0 a^2 , \\
V_3 &= V_0 + (\partial V/\partial x_2)_0 a + \tfrac{1}{2}(\partial^2 V/\partial x_2{}^2)_0 a^2 , \\
V_4 &= V_0 - (\partial V/\partial x_2)_0 a + \tfrac{1}{2}(\partial^2 V/\partial x_2{}^2)_0 a^2 , \\
V_5 &= V_0 + (\partial V/\partial x_3)_0 a + \tfrac{1}{2}(\partial^2 V/\partial x_3{}^2)_0 a^2 , \\
V_6 &= V_0 - (\partial V/\partial x_3)_0 a + \tfrac{1}{2}(\partial^2 V/\partial x_3{}^2)_0 a^2 .
\end{aligned}
\qquad (601.1)
$$

One may add the equations in (601.1) and rearrange to obtain the following difference equation approximation of the Laplacian.

$$
(\nabla^2 V)_0 = \left[\sum_{i=1}^{6} V_i - 6V_0 \right] \Big/ a^2 . \qquad (601.2)
$$

Now, let us write the equation for the current fed into the point O, using the node analysis (503.6) and Electrical Circuit Conventions III and IV, and Theorem VIII. Thus, we obtain the relation

$$C\left(6\dot{V}_0 - \sum_{i=1}^{6} \dot{V}_i\right) = \dot{q}_0 . \qquad (601.3)$$

An impulse charging current

$$\dot{q}_0 = q_0\,\delta(t) \qquad (601.4)$$

is fed into the typical branch point O. One may insert (601.4) into (601.3) and integrate with respect to the time to obtain

$$C\left(6V_0 - \sum_{i=1}^{6} V_i\right) = q_0 . \qquad (601.5)$$

Equation (601.5) may be divided through by a^2, and rearranged to yield

$$\frac{\sum_{i=1}^{6} V_i - 6V_0}{a^2} = -\left(\frac{q_0}{a^3}\right)\frac{a}{C} . \qquad (601.6)$$

If we let

$$C = \varepsilon a , \qquad (601.7)$$

Eq. (601.6) becomes the difference equation approximation of Poisson's equation, as $q_0 a^{-3}$ represents the mean charge density. Hence, taking the limit of (601.6) with $a \to 0$, gives Poisson's equation

$$\nabla^2 V = -q_v/\varepsilon . \qquad (601.8)$$

Poisson's equation has been obtained from network equations which in turn come from Hamilton's principle. Therefore Poisson's equation comes from Hamilton's principle. The generality of the method just outlined for solving Poisson's equation should be emphasized. It may be applied to any system in which the potential vanishes on the exterior boundary, and which contains conducting bodies embedded in a homogeneous isotropic medium.

Let us return to (601.5) and rewrite it in the following form

$$C_{nm}V_m = q_n. \tag{601.9}$$

Consider the reciprocal of the capacitance matrix given by

$$\Theta_{kn}C_{nm} = \delta_{km}. \tag{601.10}$$

Multiplying both sides of (601.9) on the left-hand side by the matrix Θ_{kn} gives the following solution for the voltage at any branch point of the network.

$$V_k = \Theta_{kn}q_n. \tag{601.11}$$

We will now treat the periodic network as a three-terminal network (Fig. 6.2). The potential at a particular point designated by the radius vector $\mathbf{r}_j$ is the output of the three-terminal net-

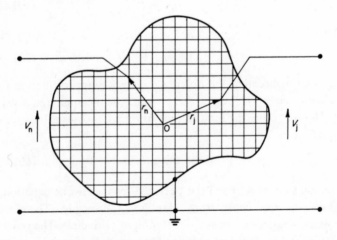

Fig. 6.2.   Three-terminal network.

work, and we are interested in the output voltage with a unit charge injected at the input, which is connected to the point designated by the radius vector $\mathbf{r}_n$. Under the conditions given, the charge distribution of the system is described by the following relation

$$q_k = 0, \qquad k \neq n, \qquad q_n = 1. \tag{601.12}$$

Hence, it follows from (601.11) and (601.12) that the voltage at the output is given by the Green's function of the network

$$V_j = \Theta_{jn}. \tag{601.13}$$

The output remains connected to the point designated by $\mathbf{r}_j$, but the input is moved from point to point, unit charge is injected and V_j determined, the input being always discharged before moving to the next point. In this way the Green's function Θ_{jn} is determined with j fixed and n representing successively all points in the system. Now take any arbitrary distribution of charge density q_k'. The potential V_j' at the point $\mathbf{r}_j$ for the charge distribution q_k' is then given by the series

$$V_j' = \sum_k \Theta_{jk} q_k'. \tag{601.14}$$

Let us now repeat the process described in connection with Eqs. (601.12)–(601.14), but we carry it out instead on the continuous system corresponding to the one just considered in the limit with $a \to 0$. We determine the Green's function of the system with a unit charge placed at the point designated by $\mathbf{r}_n$, by solving Poisson's equation with the charge density represented by the delta function $\delta(\mathbf{r}_n - \mathbf{r})$, e.g.,

$$\nabla^2 \Theta = -\delta(\mathbf{r}_n - \mathbf{r})/\varepsilon. \tag{601.15}$$

The Green's function $\Theta(\mathbf{r}_n - \mathbf{r})$ obtained from (601.15) corresponds to Θ_{jn} given by (601.13). It follows from the standard application of the Green's function, that the potential at any point designated $\mathbf{r}_j$, with the charge density of the system given by $q_v(\mathbf{r})$ is given by the following integral

$$V(\mathbf{r}_j) = \int \int \int \Theta(\mathbf{r}_j - \mathbf{r}) q_v(\mathbf{r}) \, dv. \qquad (601.16)$$

The above integral corresponds to the limit of the sum (601.14). Hence, we see that the Green's function obtained by the solution of (601.15) amounts to obtaining the proper coefficients Θ_{jk} in (601.14), and the use of the Green's function Θ_{jn} or $\Theta(\mathbf{r}_j - \mathbf{r})$ with the principle of superposition, yields the potential for any charge distribution, either by the sum (601.14) or the corresponding integral (601.16).

We have been discussing a conservative static system $(U = V_i C_{ij} V_j / 2, \quad T = 0)$, by means of which the potential may be determined for a group of conducting bodies embedded in a homogeneous isotropic medium with a fixed potential on the exterior boundary. This treatment of the potential problem converts those questions as to the existence and uniqueness of a solution into questions as to the reliability of nature to behave consistently, and therefore predictably. As every potential problem may be represented by a system in stable equilibrium, the solution must always exist and be unique. Although the sophistication with which we have considered the existence of a solution is on the level of Dr. Samuel Johnson's proof for the existence of a stone by kicking it with his foot, it will probably suffice for most of us who are preoccupied with physics and engineering.

Consider the network obtained by replacing each capacitor in Fig. 6.1 by a conductance G, to give another type of periodic network with cubic symmetry. The resulting network may be used also to represent conducting bodies within a homogeneous isotropic medium. As before, the exterior boundary of the system is grounded. Consider the current fed into the branch point O. Electrical Circuit Conventions III and IV and Theorem VIII are used to obtain the following statement.

$$G\left(6V_0 - \sum_{i=1}^{6} V_i\right) = \dot{q}_0.$$ (601.17)

By dividing both sides of (601.17) by a^2 and rearranging, one may obtain the relation

$$\frac{\sum_{i=1}^{6} V_i - 6V_0}{a^2} = -\left(\frac{\dot{q}_0}{a^3}\right)\frac{a}{G}.$$ (601.18)

Let

$$G = \sigma a$$ (601.19)

with σ the electrical conductivity of the homogeneous isotropic medium. The limit of the difference equation (601.18) with $a \to 0$ gives the following form of Poisson's equation,

$$\nabla^2 V = -\dot{q}_v/\sigma.$$ (601.20)

with $\dot{q}_v$ the current injected per unit volume.

Various systems corresponding to (601.17)–(601.20) have been used as analog computing networks for solving Poisson's equation (601.8). The reason that resistors are preferable to capacitors in the periodic computing network is that it is experimentally more convenient to feed current rather than charge into the branch points of the network. It is only essential that the branch points and the resistors connected between them describe the system under consideration, and it may be seen that this does not require that the size of the network, or even its physical shape, correspond to the physical system being analyzed. It is also evident that a considerable latitude in scale factors abounds permitting the selection of convenient values of conductance G, and convenient levels of currents $\dot{q}_i$ to be fed into the branch points, as well as convenient values of the separation distance a.

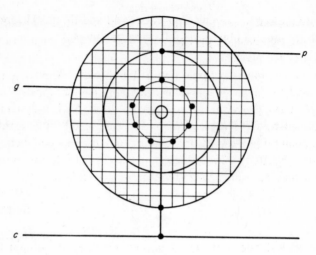

Fig. 6.3.   Representation of a triode by a periodic network with cubic symmetry.

One may use such a network to determine the potential distribution within a vacuum tube triode. Figure 6.3 represents a cross-sectional view of a network used to treat the potential within a triode. The external terminal g leads to the grid, external terminal p leads to the plate, and c connects to the cathode and conducting envelope. Consider the potential distribution within a cold triode (the filament within the cathode is turned off). As the cathode is not emitting electrons, there is no free charge within the system, so that no current is fed to the branch points of the network by the current generators. The desired potential differences between the grid, plate, and cathode are established by means of an external dc power supply. Then, the potential distribution throughout the system is determined by measuring the potential at each branch point of the network. The potential distribution within the triode with the cathode heated may be determined if the steady state electron density throughout the system is known. Given the electron density, the appropriate values of current may be fed into each branch point by the current generators. Once more, the potential distribution may be obtained by measuring the potential at each branch point of the network.

Another similar periodic network with cubic symmetry may be used to represent a system containing a homogeneous isotropic lossy dielectric, or an optic medium. Such a system is obtained by replacing each capacitor in Fig. 6.1 by a parallel combination of a capacitor satisfying (601.7) and a conductance satisfying (601.19). In this case, the current fed into the branch point may be expressed by the following statement.

$$(G + i\omega C)\left(6V_0 - \sum_{i=1}^{6} V_i\right) = \dot{q}_0 = i\omega q_0. \qquad (601.21)$$

One may divide (601.21) by a^2 and rearrange to obtain the following difference equation

$$\frac{\sum_{i=1}^{6} V_i - 6V_0}{a^2} = -\frac{q_0}{(\varepsilon - i\sigma/\omega)\,a^3}, \qquad (601.22)$$

the limit of which, with $a \to 0$, gives the following statement of Poisson's equation

$$\nabla^2 V = -\frac{q_v}{\varepsilon - i\varepsilon'} = -\frac{q_v}{\varepsilon^*}, \qquad (601.23)$$

in which the imaginary part of the permittivity represents σ/ω. By allowing the complex permittivity ε^* to be dependent on the frequency ω, the periodic network which satisfies (601.21) may be used to treat a wide class of isotropic homogeneous media at frequencies below and including the optic spectrum.

6.0.2. The Wave Equation

The propagation of an elastic longitudinal plane wave along the axis of a simple cubic crystal is a one-dimensional problem which may be treated by considering a single row of atoms in the crystal. This problem was studied by Newton, Johann Bernoulli and his son Daniel, and Baden-Powell, but it was Lord Kelvin who first gave a detailed treatment; both the solutions and the historical background to this problem have been summarized by Brillouin (1946).

Consider a linear array of atoms evenly spaced with a mean separation a. The mean position of the sth atom from the origin is given by sa, and we consider those atoms contained within unit length, for which s is confined in the range $-N/2 \leqslant s \leqslant +N/2$, with N a very large even number, e.g., $N \sim 10^8$ would be typical. Let the variation in the position of the sth atom from its mean location under an elastic wave be given by the amplitude ψ_s. Considering that each atom is effectively screened from all but its nearest neighbors, the potential energy is a function of the separation between the nearest neighbors. As the lattice is moving about an equilibrium configuration, the linear term vanishes in the expansion of potential energy U. Thus, for small amplitude vibrations, the potential energy may be written as a quadratic function of the difference in the amplitudes of neighboring atoms. The potential energy in this case is determined in the same way as required for the determination of the potential energy of the two masses coupled by springs in Chapter 4, Exercise (4.1). The potential energy density is given by the following series

$$U_v = \sum_s \tfrac{1}{2} v a (\psi_{s-1} - \psi_s)^2, \quad s = 0, \pm 1, \pm 2, \ldots, \pm N/2,$$

(602.1)

in which v is Young's modulus.

The kinetic energy of the sth atom is simply $\tfrac{1}{2} m \dot{\psi}_s{}^2$, and the kinetic energy density of the lattice is given by the sum

$$T_v = \sum_s \tfrac{1}{2} m \dot{\psi}_s{}^2, \quad s = 0, \pm 1, \pm 2, \ldots, \pm N/2. \quad (602.2)$$

Hence, we may write a Lagrangian density for the lattice,

$\mathscr{L}_v = T_v - U_v$ by taking the difference between (602.2) and (602.1), e.g.,

$$\mathscr{L}_v = \sum_s \left[\tfrac{1}{2} m\dot{\psi}_s^2 - \tfrac{1}{2} va(\psi_{s-1} - \psi_s)^2\right]. \qquad (602.3)$$

By applying Theorem I to (602.3), we obtain the following equations of motion

$$m\ddot{\psi}_s - va(\psi_{s-1} - 2\psi_s + \psi_{s+1}) = 0. \qquad (602.4)$$

By rearranging (602.4) and dividing through by a^2, we have the relation

$$(\psi_{s-1} - 2\psi_s + \psi_{s+1})/a^2 = (m/va^3)\ddot{\psi}_s \qquad (602.5)$$

One may show that (602.5) is the difference form of the wave equation simply by adding the first two expressions in (601.1) and rearranging. Hence, taking the limit of (602.5) with $a \to 0$ gives the differential wave equation

$$\frac{\partial^2 \psi}{\partial x^2} = \frac{\rho}{v} \frac{\partial^2 \psi}{\partial t^2}, \qquad (602.6)$$

in which ρ is the mean density obtained by averaging the mass m over a cube with volume a^3. The wave equation (602.6) refers to a uniform continuous medium, and its solutions indicate that waves propagate through the medium with constant phase velocity, i.e., the ratio of frequency to wave vector ω/k is independent of frequency. However, the density of the lattice is not uniform but varies periodically with period a, and therefore its behavior can be expected to follow the solutions of (602.5) more closely than those of (602.6). On top of the periodicity of the lattice we impose the Born-Kármán boundary conditions (see Chapter 2, Section 2.1.0) making the amplitude function ψ_s periodic in length with Na the fundamental period. Thus, we may express the amplitude of the elastic waves in the crystal by the Fourier series

$$\psi(t, sa) = \sum_k C_k \exp i(ksa - \omega t), \qquad (602.7)$$

in which we have the fundamental wave vector k_0 based on the fundamental period Na, e.g.,

$$k_0 = 2\pi(Na)^{-1}, \qquad (602.8)$$

with the wave vector given by

$$k = lk_0, \qquad (602.9)$$

where l is confined within the range from $-N/2$ to $+N/2$. As the equations of motion (602.4) are linear, the principle of superposition applies, and it follows from Theorem IV that it is sufficient to solve (602.5) for a single term in (602.7). Hence, we substitute $C_k (\exp) i(ksa - \omega t)$ for ψ_s in (602.5), and after canceling like factors on both sides of the equation, we obtain the relation

$$(e^{-ika} - 2 + e^{ika})/a^2 = -\omega^2 \rho/v, \qquad (602.10)$$

which reduces to

$$[(2 \sin \tfrac{1}{2} ka)/a]^2 = \omega^2 \rho/v. \qquad (602.11)$$

Considering only positive values of the frequency, we have the relationship between the frequency and wave vector of

$$\omega(k) = (2/a)(v/\rho)^{\frac{1}{2}} |\sin \tfrac{1}{2} ka|, \qquad (602.12)$$

or the equivalent expression

$$\omega(l) = (2/a)(v/\rho)^{\frac{1}{2}} |\sin (l\pi/N)|, \qquad l = 0, \pm 1, \pm 2, \ldots, \pm N/2. \qquad (602.13)$$

The solution $\omega(k)$ as given by either (602.12) or (602.13) indicates that the lattice can propagate waves only in a band of closely spaced eigenvalues of frequency[†] with an upper limit $\omega_{max} = (2/a)(v/\rho)^{\frac{1}{2}}$. Obviously, the relationship between the frequency ω and wave vector k depends upon the distribution of density within the elastic medium. If the density is uniform so that (602.6) is obeyed, then the frequency ω is a continuous linear function of the wave vector k, but if the density varies periodically and (602.5) is obeyed, then the relation between the frequency ω and wave vector k is given instead by (602.12). Furthermore, it follows that both the *phase velocity* ω/k, and the *group velocity* $d\omega/dk$, become frequency-dependent when the periodicity of the density is taken into account, i.e., the periodicity of the lattice is responsible for the phenomenon of *dispersion*. Both the phase velocity

$$\omega/k = (v/\rho)^{\frac{1}{2}}|\sin\tfrac{1}{2}ka|/\tfrac{1}{2}ka, \qquad (602.14)$$

and the group velocity

$$d\omega/dk = (v/\rho)^{\frac{1}{2}}\cos\tfrac{1}{2}ka, \qquad (602.15)$$

have the same limiting value $(v/\rho)^{\frac{1}{2}}$ for very large wavelengths, which is the same as the constant velocity indicated in (602.6).

For frequencies exceeding the cutoff, the wave vector becomes complex, and we may write

$$k = \pm\{(\pi/a) + i\beta\}. \qquad (602.16)$$

By inserting (602.16) into (602.10) one may obtain the relation

$$\cosh\tfrac{1}{2}\beta a = \omega/\omega_{max}, \qquad (602.17)$$

[†] The discrete values of $\omega(k)$ may be compared with the individual spectral amplitudes (210.8) of the Fourier series, which merge to form the continuous curve (210.14) of the Fourier integral as N approaches infinity. Thus, although $\omega(k)$ is not a continuous function, it still resembles one with N very large, because the limit of $\omega(k)$ with N approaching infinity is a continuous function.

which yields for the relaxation length

$$1/\beta = a/\{\ln[\Phi + (\Phi^2 - 1)^{\frac{1}{2}}]\}, \qquad (602.17a)$$

with

$$\Phi = 2(\omega/\omega_{max})^2 - 1. \qquad (602.17b)$$

Obviously, a relaxation length $\beta^{-1} = a$ represents an upper limit of attenuation with our analytical model, which occurs with $\omega = 1.043\omega_{max}$. Thus, the amplitudes of elastic waves are very

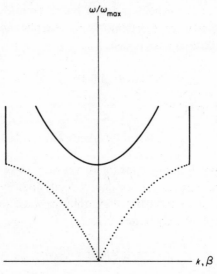

Fig. 6.4. The normalized frequency ω/ω_{max} is shown as a dotted curve in the pass band of frequencies, and as a continuous curve for frequencies exceeding the cutoff ω_{max}.

sharply attenuated with distance in the lattice for frequencies which exceed the cutoff frequency ω_{max} by just a small fraction of the bandwidth.

The relationship between the frequency ω and the wave vector k is shown in Fig. 6.4; the dotted and solid lines indicate respectively that the function $\omega(k)$ has discrete values in the pass band $0 \leqslant \omega \leqslant \omega_{max}$, and is a continuous function above the pass band $\omega_{max} < \omega$.

There is another method of taking the periodicity of the lattice density into account which should be mentioned. For example, taking the steady-state solution of (602.6) by letting $\psi(x, t) = e^{i\omega t}\psi(x)$, makes (602.6) reduce to the ordinary differential equation

$$\frac{d^2\psi}{dx^2} + \frac{\omega^2\rho}{v}\,\psi = 0. \qquad (602.18)$$

Now, we treat the periodicity in the density by having ρ in (602.18) become a periodic function with the periodicity of the lattice, e.g., we let

$$\rho(x) = \rho(x + sa). \qquad (602.19)$$

The differential equation (602.18) assumes a well-known form, viz., Hill's equation, with the density $\rho(x)$ given by (602.19). It follows by Floquet's theorem that the solution of Hill's equation is of the following form

$$\psi(x) = e^{ikx}u(x), \qquad (602.20)$$

with

$$u(x) = u(x + sa). \qquad (602.21)$$

When the Born-Kármán conditions are used, k in (602.20) is given by (602.8) and (602.9). It should be noticed that the admissible values of k for a periodic system are the same whether we use Hill's equation or the difference wave equation as they depend entirely upon the Born-Kármán conditions. The solutions of Hill's equation can be expected to provide more detailed information than those of the difference equation. This may be understood by considering how to obtain an approximate solution of Hill's equation by using difference equations. Quite a few simultaneous difference equations referred to the region about a typical atom would obviously be required in place of our solitary relation (602.5) to bring out the distinction between the two methods. It turns out that whereas the single difference equation (602.5) gives a single pass band of frequencies, the solutions of Hill's equation provide many pass bands, which may either overlap or may be separated by frequency intervals in which waves cannot propagate.

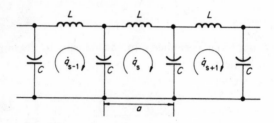

Fig. 6.5. Low pass filter.

Consider the ideal (lossless) low pass electric filter shown in Fig. 6.5. Assuming the filter to be composed of many sections, it may be represented exactly by Eqs. (602.1)–(602.17) by replacing ψ_s by q_s, va by C^{-1}, and m by L. In the filter, the potential energy density (602.1) refers to the energy stored in the electric fields, the energy which is localized within the capacitors, and the kinetic energy density (602.2) refers to the energy stored in the magnetic fields, the energy localized in the coils. As with the mechanical lattice, the quadratic functions of the amplitudes (602.1) and (602.2) fluctuate periodically throughout the structure. Whereas the uniform elastic material that is supposed to obey (602.6) is not very well approximated in nature, the corresponding limiting case of the low pass electric filter is merely the common transmission line. The energy density stored in the electric and magnetic fields around a transmission line, given by

(602.1) and (602.2), is not distributed periodically but rather uniformly along its length. Consequently, the transmission line obeys (602.6), and exhibits neither a cutoff frequency nor dispersion.

6.0.3. Symmetric Filters

Consider a periodic filter network composed of a series of identical three-terminal networks (Fig. 5.22) connected in cascade. Each three-terminal network has an admittance matrix

$$\begin{pmatrix} y_{11} & y_{12} \\ y_{12} & y_{11} \end{pmatrix}. \tag{603.1}$$

We are considering only lossless filters here, so that the admittance elements y_{ij} are all pure imaginary. The additional restriction is made that the three-terminal networks are symmetric, i.e., the input and output are indistinguishable making $y_{11} = y_{22}$. Electric filters in this class may be considered as analogs of a one-dimensional crystal with the three-terminal network playing the role of the unit cell. Let an admittance Y_0 be connected across the output terminals of the filter. It follows from Theorem X that the input and output voltage are related to the input current by the following matrix equation.

$$\begin{pmatrix} y_{11} & y_{12} \\ y_{12} & (y_{11} + Y_0) \end{pmatrix} \begin{pmatrix} v_1 \\ v_2 \end{pmatrix} = \begin{pmatrix} \dot{q}_1 \\ 0 \end{pmatrix}. \tag{603.2}$$

If the input admittance $\dot{q}_1/v_1$ equals Y_0, then the three-terminal network at the output may be replaced by Y_0 itself with no effect on the remainder of the filter circuit. Hence, it follows that this unique value of Y_0 equals the input admittance of the filter with any number of unit cells; it is called the *characteristic admittance* of the filter. By solving (603.2) for the input admittance one obtains the expression

$$\frac{\dot{q}_1}{v_1} = y_{11} - \frac{y_{12}^2}{y_{11} + Y_0}. \tag{603.3}$$

Then by equating (603.3) to Y_0 and solving for Y_0, one may obtain the characteristic admittance

$$Y_0 = \sqrt{|y|}, \tag{603.4}$$

in which $|y|$ is the determinant of the admittance matrix of the unit cell (603.1). As the impedance matrix (z) of the unit cell is the inverse of (603.1), it follows that the characteristic impedance Z_0 may be written

$$Z_0 = \sqrt{|z|}. \tag{603.5}$$

As the filter is lossless, the gain per unit cell is simply a phase factor $e^{-i\theta}$ in the pass bands, and it is this relation that defines the boundaries of the pass bands. For example, the voltage gain per unit cell comes from (603.2) by inspection and may be written

$$\exp[-(\beta + i\theta)] = -y_{12}/(y_{11} + \sqrt{|y|}) \tag{603.6}$$

in which $\beta = 0$ in the pass bands. Therefore, in the pass bands we have

$$\exp[\pm i\theta] = -y_{12}/(y_{11} \pm \sqrt{|y|}), \tag{603.7}$$

in which propagation in both directions is taken into account by writing the phase as $\pm\theta$, and the characteristic admittance as $\pm\sqrt{|y|}$. Proceeding from (603.7) we may write

$$\cos\theta \pm i\sin\theta = -y_{12}(y_{11} \mp \sqrt{|y|})/(y_{11}^2 - |y|), \tag{603.8}$$

$$= (-y_{11} \pm \sqrt{|y|})/y_{12}, \tag{603.9}$$

or

$$\cos\theta \pm i\sin\theta = (z_{11} \mp \sqrt{|z|})/z_{12}. \tag{603.10}$$

Since y_{11} and y_{12} are pure imaginary and $\sqrt{|y|}$ is real in the pass bands, it follows then that the cosine term may be written separately as follows

$$\cos \theta = -y_{11}/y_{12} = z_{11}/z_{12} \quad \text{(in the pass bands).} \quad (603.11)$$

Therefore, the pass bands are defined by the following range:

$$-1 < z_{11}/z_{12} < +1. \quad (603.12)$$

The low pass filter (Fig. 6.5) may be composed of either a series of cascade connected T sections (Fig. 6.6), or a series of

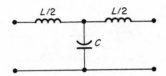

Fig. 6.6.   A low pass filter T-section.

cascade connected Π-sections (Fig. 6.7), and it is interesting to note that these two examples of the low pass filter do not have the same characteristic impedance. The limiting case of a low

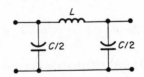

Fig. 6.7.   A low pass filter Π-section.

pass filter with $a \to 0$ (Fig. 6.5) is a transmission line, and in this limiting case the distinction between the T- and Π-sections disappears. Thus, it follows that the characteristic impedance of a transmission line is the same as that of a low pass filter of either T- or Π-sections in the low frequency range in which dispersion is negligible.

6.0.4. Transmission Lines

Consider a uniform transmission line with constant values of both impedance per unit length z and admittance per unit length y. A schematic circuit diagram for an incremental section of the transmission line between x and $x + \Delta x$ is shown in Fig. 6.8. We start by considering the transmission line to extend on the right to infinity, and we are going to determine what the impedance of this infinite line would be if it were broken at x and a measurement made at that point. It may be seen by Fig. 6.8

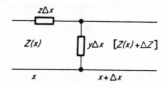

Fig. 6.8. An incremental section of a transmission line.

that the impedance $Z(x)$ consists of the impedance $z\,\Delta x$ in series with the parallel combination of the admittance $y\,\Delta x$ and the admittance $[Z(x) + \Delta Z]^{-1}$. Hence, we may write

$$Z(x) = z\,\Delta x + [y\,\Delta x + (Z(x) + \Delta Z)^{-1}]^{-1} \quad (604.1)$$

If we expand (604.1) and retain only the linear terms in Δx and ΔZ, we have

$$Z(x) = z\,\Delta x + Z(x) + \Delta Z - y\,[Z(x)]^2\,\Delta x, \quad (604.2)$$

which reduces to the expression

$$\Delta Z/\Delta x = y\,[Z(x)]^2 - z. \quad (604.3)$$

Taking the limit with $\Delta x \to 0$, gives the following differential equation for the impedance of a transmission line, e.g.,

$$dZ/dx = \lim_{\Delta x \to 0} (\Delta Z/\Delta x) = y\,[Z(x)]^2 - z \qquad (604.4)$$

The impedance $Z(x)$ at any location along an infinite line cannot be a function of x, but must be a constant Z_0, which depends on the properties of the line. This constant Z_0 is the characteristic impedance of the transmission line. Therefore, with an infinite line, (604.4) reduces to

$$yZ_0^{\,2} - z = 0, \qquad (604.5)$$

which yields the characteristic impedance

$$Z_0 = (z/y)^{\frac{1}{2}}. \qquad (604.6)$$

If the transmission line were not to extend on the right to infinity, but instead to a finite length terminated in its characteristic impedance Z_0, one could not tell the difference by measurements made at the point x. Thus, when terminated in its characteristic impedance Z_0, a transmission line behaves as an infinite line, and signals cannot be reflected from its termination. When a transmission line is terminated in its characteristic impedance it is said to be *matched*.

The circuit diagram in Fig. 6.8 is now used to calculate the complex wave vector k^* of the steady-state ac voltage along a matched line. The circuit is a simple voltage divider, so that the fraction of the total voltage appearing across the impedance $z\,\Delta x$ equals the ratio of $z\,\Delta x$ to the total impedance Z_0, e.g.,

$$\Delta V/V(x) = -z\,\Delta x/Z_0 \qquad (604.7)$$

By taking the limit of (604.7) with $\Delta x \to 0$ and rearranging, one obtains the following differential equation

$$(dV/dx) + (zy)^{\frac{1}{2}}V = 0, \qquad (604.8)$$

which has the well known solution

$$V(x) = V(0) \exp[-(zy)^{\frac{1}{2}}x] \qquad (604.9)$$

It may be seen from (604.9) that a matched transmission line has a complex wave vector

$$k^* = -i(zy)^{\frac{1}{2}}. \qquad (604.10)$$

Consider a transmission line of finite length l, terminated in an impedance $Z_l \neq Z_0$. The input impedance $Z(0)$ will be determined by solving the differential equation (604.4) with the terminating impedance Z_l at the end of the line as a boundary condition. By substituting (604.6) into (604.4) and rearranging, we have the relation

$$dZ/(Z^2 - Z_0{}^2) = y\,dx, \qquad (604.11)$$

which may be rewritten by partial fractions as follows

$$\frac{dZ}{Z - Z_0} - \frac{dZ}{Z + Z_0} = 2(zy)^{\frac{1}{2}}dx \qquad (604.12)$$

or

$$d\left[\ln\left(\frac{Z - Z_0}{Z + Z_0}\right)\right] = 2(zy)^{\frac{1}{2}}dx. \qquad (604.13)$$

Equation (604.13) is now integrated from the end of the line $(x = l)$ where it terminates in the impedance Z_l to the input $(x = 0)$ at which the impedance is $Z(0)$.

$$\ln\left[\Gamma\left(\frac{Z(0) + Z_0}{Z(0) - Z_0}\right)\right] = 2(zy)^{\frac{1}{2}}l \qquad (604.14)$$

in which Γ stands for $(Z_l - Z_0)/Z_l + Z_0)$, the *voltage reflection coefficient* (see Exercise 6.4). One may easily solve the transcendental relation (604.14) to obtain as the expression for the input impedance

$$Z(0) = Z_0 \left(\frac{1 + \Gamma \exp(-2(zy)^{\frac{1}{2}}l)}{1 - \Gamma \exp(-2(zy)^{\frac{1}{2}}l)} \right). \qquad (604.15)$$

Consider the transient response of a short circuited line, $Z_l = 0$, which is matched at the input (Fig. 6.9). This example

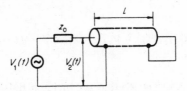

Fig. 6.9. A transmission line which is matched at the input and short circuited at the output.

is of interest because the shorted line has found wide use as a pulse clipping device. As the line is short circuited the voltage reflection coefficient may be written simply as $\Gamma = -1$. The line is considered here to be lossless so that we may write $z = i\omega L$ and $y = i\omega C$. Hence, for a shorted lossless line, expression (604.15) reduces to

$$Z(0) = Z_0 \left(\frac{1 - \exp(-i2\omega(LC)^{\frac{1}{2}}l)}{1 + \exp(-i2\omega(LC)^{\frac{1}{2}}l)} \right). \qquad (604.16)$$

The response of the line $V_2(t)$ to an incident pulse $V_1(t)$ may be easily determined from (604.16) by the following argument. The Laplace transform impedance of the line is obtained by substituting ζ for $i\omega$ in (604.16), e.g.,

$$Z(0) = Z_0 \left(\frac{1 - \exp(-2(LC)^{\frac{1}{2}}l\zeta)}{1 + \exp(-2(LC)^{\frac{1}{2}}l\zeta)} \right). \qquad (604.17)$$

The line and the series impedance Z_0 form a voltage divider

(Fig. 6.9). Thus the Laplace transform of $V_1(t)$ and $V_2(t)$ are related as follows:

$$V_2(\zeta) = \frac{Z(0) V_1(\zeta)}{Z(0) + Z_0}, \tag{604.18}$$

$$= \tfrac{1}{2} V_1(\zeta) [1 - \exp(-2(LC)^{\frac{1}{2}} l\zeta)]. \tag{604.19}$$

The solution of (604.19) is given by Heaviside's shifting theorem (210.41).

$$V_2(t) = \tfrac{1}{2} [V_1(t) H(t) - V_1(t - 2(LC)^{\frac{1}{2}} l) H(t - 2(LC)^{\frac{1}{2}} l)], \tag{604.20}$$

It may be seen by (604.20) that the incident pulse is opposed by its echo which arrives in time $2(LC)^{\frac{1}{2}} \cdot l$.

Some of the characteristics of standing waves on a mismatched transmission line are reviewed in the remainder of this section, and the discussion centers about the relationship between the voltage reflection coefficient and the impedance terminating the line. The complex plane of the impedance and the complex plane of the reflection coefficient may be conveniently related through the principles of conformal mapping by the well known *Smith chart* (Smith, 1939). We will now discuss the use of the Smith chart to determine the terminating impedance of a transmission line from measurements made with a slotted line.

The voltage measured on a slotted line at position x is given by the following expression,[†]

$$V(x) = V_+ [1 + \Gamma \exp\{-i2k(l - x)\}] \tag{604.21}$$

in which V_+ is the amplitude of the voltage wave incident on the termination, and $x = l$ is the location of the termination of the line. It may be seen that a wave traveling from point x down the line to the termination and back to the point x undergoes a phase

---

† It is assumed that the losses within the slotted line are negligible.

shift $2k(l - x)$. Thus, the voltage at the point x as given by (604.21), consists of the voltage amplitude of the incident wave V_+ added to the voltage amplitude of the reflected wave $V_+ \Gamma \exp\{-i2k(l - x)\}$. It is convenient to write the voltage reflection coefficient as follows,

$$\Gamma = (\xi - 1)/(\xi + 1), \qquad (604.22)$$

in which the normalized terminating impedance is given by the expression,

$$\xi = Z_l/Z_0, \qquad (604.23)$$

with Z_l the terminating impedance, and Z_0 the characteristic impedance of the line. It is convenient in the following discussion to write the normalized terminating impedance as

$$\xi = \rho + i\gamma, \qquad (604.24)$$

and to express the voltage reflection coefficient as the product of its magnitude $|\Gamma|$ and the phase factor $e^{i\theta}$, e.g.,

$$\Gamma = |\Gamma| e^{i\theta}. \qquad (604.25)$$

Dividing both sides of (604.21) by V_+ gives the normalized voltage, and the two terms of this expression are given by the geometric construction shown in Fig. 6.10. The term "standing

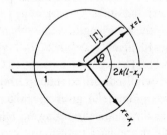

Fig. 6.10. Geometric construction showing the normalized voltage on a transmission line.

wave ratio" has widespread usage, and it is defined by the following expression

$$S = V_{max}/V_{min} \qquad (604.26)$$

It is clear by the geometric construction shown in Fig. 6.10 and Eq. (604.21) that the standing wave ratio may be written

$$S = (1 + |\Gamma|)/(1 - |\Gamma|). \qquad (604.27)$$

Obviously, when the termination of the line is short circuited, the voltage must vanish. Therefore, the reflection coefficient for the short circuit termination must equal -1 to make the reflected wave cancel out the incident wave; this checks with (604.22) in which ξ vanishes with a short circuit termination. By measuring the voltage against distance on the slotted line, first with the termination a short circuit, and second with some finite impedance terminating the line, the phase θ of the reflection coefficient may be determined by the displacement between the minimas of the two different voltage measurements. By plotting the voltage against the distance, it may be seen that the location of the minima are more sharply defined than the locations of the maxima. Thus, more use is made of the minima than the maxima. It may be verified by Fig. 6.10 that the distance between two minima corresponds to a phase shift $2k(l-x)$ of 2π. Thus, the distance between the minima $(l-x)$ equals a half wavelength, so that this distance determined experimentally is used to determine the wavelength. Some schematic illustrations of voltage measured against distance with a slotted line are shown in Fig. 6.11. The central pattern, S.C., refers to the voltage measured with a short circuited termination. The displacement of the minima (l') gives the phase of the voltage reflection coefficient through the following relation.

$$\theta = \frac{\pi}{2} - \frac{4\pi l'}{\lambda} \qquad (604.28)$$

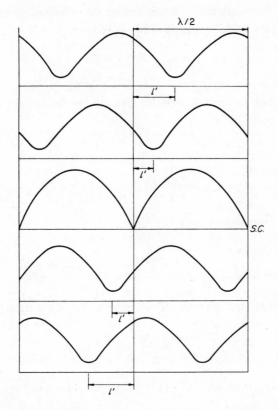

Fig. 6.11. Schematic illustration of standing waves of voltage on a mismatched transmission line for several cases; the curve marked S.C. refers to a short circuited termination.

We have considered the locus of normalized voltage in the complex plane, e.g.,

$$V(x)/V_+ = 1 + \Gamma \exp[-i2k(l - x)] \qquad (604.29)$$

as illustrated by Fig. 6.10. We now consider the locus of the reflection coefficient itself (604.25) in the complex plane in terms of some alternative expressions which are useful in connection with the Smith chart. We first write the reflection coefficient by inserting (604.24) into (604.22) as follows.

$$\Gamma = \frac{\rho - 1 + i\gamma}{\rho + 1 + i\gamma}. \qquad (604.30)$$

We then manipulate (604.30) through the following steps.

$$\Gamma = \frac{-2 + \rho + 1 + i\gamma}{\rho + 1 + i\gamma} = 1 - \frac{2}{\rho + 1 + i\gamma}$$

$$= 1 - \frac{2}{\rho + 1}\left(1 + \frac{i\gamma}{\rho + 1}\right)^{-1}.$$

The expression

$$\left(1 + \frac{i\gamma}{\rho + 1}\right)^{-1} = \tfrac{1}{2}(1 + e^{-i2\varphi}), \qquad \text{with } \tan \varphi = \gamma/(\rho + 1),$$
$$(604.31)$$

is inserted in the above and we arrive at the following expression.

$$\Gamma = \frac{\rho}{\rho + 1} - \frac{e^{-i2\varphi}}{\rho + 1}. \qquad (604.32)$$

We now consider ρ as a parameter, and allow γ to vary over the

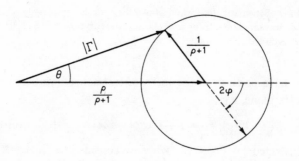

Fig. 6.12.   Voltage reflection coefficient on a circle with ρ as the parameter.

range $-\infty < \gamma < \infty$. We have a set of circles for each value of the parameter ρ; a typical construction is shown in Fig. 6.12. We now return to the expression for the voltage reflection coefficient as given by (604.30) and proceed to manipulate it as before with a slight modification as indicated below.

$$\Gamma = 1 - \frac{2}{\rho + 1 + i\gamma}$$
$$= 1 + \frac{i2}{\gamma\left[1 - \left[i(\rho + 1)/\gamma\right]\right]} .$$

This time we obtain the following expressions:

$$\Gamma = 1 + (i/\gamma)(1 + e^{i2\eta}) \qquad (604.33)$$

and

$$\tan \eta = \cot \varphi = (\rho + 1)/\gamma . \qquad (604.34)$$

In this instance we take γ as the parameter, and permit ρ to vary over the range $0 < \rho < \infty$. For each value of the parameter γ, the locus of the reflection coefficient describes a circle; a typical construction is shown in Fig. 6.13. It may be seen that with a

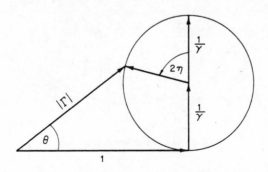

Fig. 6.13. Voltage reflection coefficient on a circle with γ as the parameter.

terminating impedance $\rho_1 + i\gamma_1$, the reflection coefficient Γ_1 terminates in the complex plane at the intersection of the circle given by (604.32) with $\rho = \rho_1$, and the circle given by (604.33) with $\gamma = \gamma_1$. Since we are interested only in the intersections of the circles given by (604.32) and (604.33), and the circle given by (604.32) cannot have a radius exceeding unity, we need only those parts of the circles given by (604.33) which lie within the circle with radius unity; the resulting construction is called the Smith chart (Fig. 6.14). The Smith chart is designed to corre-

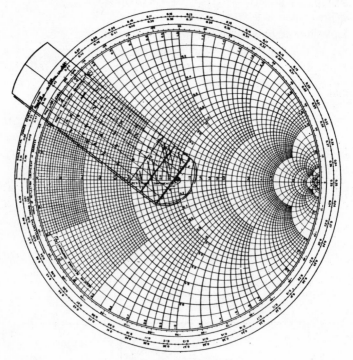

Fig. 6.14.   The Smith chart.[†]

[†] Smith charts, either in the form of a slide rule or graph paper, are available from The Emeloid Co., Inc., 1239 Central Ave., Hillside, New Jersey 07205.

spond to the construction shown in Fig. 6.10, and at the same
time to give the terminating impedance according to relations
(604.31)–(604.34). It may be seen that the Smith chart is bisym-
metric, the real axis being the axis of symmetry.

Given the magnitude and the phase of the voltage reflection
coefficient, the normalized terminating impedance is immediately given by the Smith chart; the locus of the voltage reflection
coefficient coincides with the intersection of two circles, one
giving ρ, the normalized terminating resistance, and the other
giving γ, the normalized terminating reactance. Therefore, an
experimental determination of the voltage reflection coefficient
may be used to obtain the terminating impedance through the
use of the Smith chart. A measurement of the standing wave
ratio gives the magnitude of the voltage reflection coefficient
through the following relation,

$$| \Gamma | = (S - 1)/(S + 1), \qquad (604.35)$$

which comes directly from (604.27). The phase of the voltage
reflection coefficient is given by the displacement of the minima
and relation (604.28), as discussed earlier. The quadrant in which
the voltage reflection coefficient is located may be easily recognized by solving (604.30) explicitly for the phase θ. The following
expressions are readily obtained from (604.30).

$$\Gamma = \frac{\rho^2 + \gamma^2 - 1 + i2\gamma}{(\rho + 1)^2 + \gamma^2}$$

$$= \frac{e^{i\theta}([\rho^2 + \gamma^2 - 1]^2 + 4\gamma^2)^{\frac{1}{2}}}{(\rho + 1)^2 + \gamma^2}, \qquad (604.36)$$

$$\tan \theta = \frac{2\gamma}{\rho^2 + \gamma^2 - 1}. \qquad (604.37)$$

It follows by inspection from (604.36) and (604.37) that if

$$\rho^2 + \gamma^2 > 1, \quad \gamma > 0, \qquad \Gamma \text{ falls in the first quadrant,}$$

if $\rho^2 + \gamma^2 < 1$, $\gamma > 0$, Γ falls in the second quadrant,
if $\rho^2 + \gamma^2 < 1$, $\gamma < 0$, Γ falls in the third quadrant,
and if $\rho^2 + \gamma^2 > 1$, $\gamma < 0$, Γ falls in the fourth quadrant.

There is much more to the Smith chart than meets the eye, and its use extends considerably beyond the applications mentioned here. It will suffice, then, to close this section by adding one of the more common applications; it will be explained how to determine the impedance of a transmission line of given length and terminating impedance.

Consider the following function of x.

$$\Gamma(x) = \Gamma \exp[-i2k(l-x)]. \qquad (604.38)$$

The function $\Gamma(x)$ reduces to the voltage reflection coefficient for $x = l$. It follows from (604.15) that the normalized impedance at the point x may be written

$$\xi(x) = \frac{Z(x)}{Z_0} = \frac{1 + \Gamma(x)}{1 - \Gamma(x)}. \qquad (604.39)$$

The following expression is obtained by solving (604.39) for the function $\Gamma(x)$.

$$\Gamma(x) = \frac{\xi(x) - 1}{\xi(x) + 1}. \qquad (604.40)$$

Comparing (604.22) with (604.40), it may be seen that the arguments given with relations (604.30)–(604.34) apply equally well with relation (604.39). Therefore, the locus of the voltage reflection coefficient on the Smith chart may also define the normalized impedance of a transmission line with length $(l - x)$ and a terminating impedance Z_l. One uses the Smith chart in the following manner to obtain the normalized impedance $\xi(x)$. First, one locates the voltage reflection coefficient of the terminating impedance at the appropriate intersection of the two circles giving ρ the normalized terminating resistance, and γ the normalized terminating reactance. Then, one rotates the reflection coefficient clockwise through the angle $2k(l-x)$, maintaining a constant radius. The new location of the reflection coefficient falls on the intersection of two circles, which give the real and imaginary parts of the normalized impedance $\xi(x)$.

6.0.5. Circuit Models of Classical Electromagnetic Radiation

By treating the ratio of the electric to magnetic field as an impedance, Schelkunoff (1938) developed methods of handling wave propagation that have been very effective in radar engineering. The utility of his methods was demonstrated in World War II, and summarized after the conflict by Booker (1947). These methods are now commonly presented in engineering texts on electromagnetic radiation (Adler *et al.*, 1960).

In a homogeneous, isotropic medium with permittivity ε and permeability μ, the ratio of the electric field E to the magnetic field H defines a characteristic wave impedance

$$Z_0 = E/H = (\mu/\varepsilon)^{\frac{1}{2}} \qquad (605.1)$$

which equals ~ 377 ohms in vacuo; the wave vector is given by

$$k = \omega (\mu\varepsilon)^{\frac{1}{2}}. \qquad (605.2)$$

Losses in the medium may be accounted for by letting ε and μ become complex. A plane wave traversing medium 1 and encountering medium 2 on a plane boundary at normal incidence may be treated the same as the problem of wave propagation at the junction between two different transmission lines; (605.1) and (605.2) are substituted for the characteristic impedance and wave vector, and E and H for V and $\dot{q}$ respectively.

If the wave meets the boundary at oblique incidence, it is separated as usual into two components (E_e, H_e) in which E_e is in the plane of the boundary and (E_h, H_h) in which H_h is in the plane of the boundary. On either side of the boundary, the ratios E_e/H_e and E_h/H_h equal the characteristic impedance of the medium. It follows that the component (E_e/H_e) has a characteristic impedance in the plane of the boundary

$$Z_{ei} = (\mu_i/\varepsilon_i)^{\frac{1}{2}} \sec \theta_i, \qquad (605.3)$$

with $i = 1$ and 2, referring to medium 1 and medium 2 respectively, which makes θ_1 the angle of incidence and reflection and θ_2 the angle of refraction. The corresponding impedance for the component (E_h, H_h) is given by the expression,

$$Z_{hi} = (\mu_i/\varepsilon_i)^{\frac{1}{2}} \cos \theta_i. \qquad (605.4)$$

In order for continuity conditions to hold everywhere across the boundary, it is necessary that they include the component of the wave vector in the plane of the boundary. Thus, we have

$$k_1 \sin \theta_1 = k_2 \sin \theta_2, \qquad (605.5)$$

which is Snell's law. One obtains Fresnel's equations by substituting (605.3) and (605.4) into the reflection and transmission coefficients for the junction between two transmission lines (see Exercise 6.4). These relations reveal that the Brewster angle is that unique angle at which there is an impedance match between the two media traversed by the radiation, whereas the critical angle is that at which the impedance and wave vector both become imaginary across the interface (Booker, 1947). Thus, the critical angle shares common features with a filter, because the characteristic impedance and wave vector in a filter become imaginary in the frequency reject bands.

It turns out that a wave traversing several plane slabs of

different optic media may be treated in the same way as a wave traversing several lengths of different transmission lines; in such a problem, expression (604.15) gives the impedance of a slab of finite thickness.

For a given separation between open conductors the radiation leakage increases with decreasing wavelength. Thus, for the transmission of microwaves, closed systems such as coaxial cables and wave guides are appropriate. As the lateral dimensions are not small compared with a wavelength, wave guides may exhibit propagation in a variety of modes, dispersion and a frequency cutoff. The ratio of the components of the electric field and magnetic field in the plane of the cross section of the wave guide may be treated as a characteristic wave impedance. The characteristic wave impedance and wave vector for a particular mode of an H_1 wave in a rectangular guide may be written

$$Z_0 = \left[\frac{\mu}{\varepsilon}\bigg/\left(1 - \frac{\omega_c^2}{\omega^2}\right)\right]^{\frac{1}{2}} \tag{605.6}$$

and

$$k = \omega\left[\mu\varepsilon\left(1 - \frac{\omega_c^2}{\omega^2}\right)\right]^{\frac{1}{2}}, \tag{605.7}$$

in which ω_c is the cutoff frequency for the particular mode. There is no propagation below the cutoff frequency, because both the impedance and wave vector become imaginary. Booker (1947) has shown that the behavior of H_1 waves in rectangular waveguides may be treated by substituting (605.6) and (605.7) into formulas for transmission lines, and he has demonstrated how the wave impedance method also provides helpful ways of looking at Babinet's principle, the behavior of antenna arrays and optical gratings.

There is another circuit model for treating the propagation of classical radiation which should be considered. This model was developed by Kron (1943, 1944), and has been employed by

Whinnery and Ramo (1944), Whinnery *et al.*, (1944), and
McAllister (1944). In Kron's method, space is represented by a
periodic network with cubic symmetry. A representative section
of the lattice is shown in Fig. 6.15. The point in the diagram

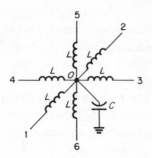

Fig. 6.15. Typical branch of a three-dimensional low pass filter with
cubic symmetry.

designated O represents an arbitrary point in the vacuum. The
point O is connected to its six nearest neighbors in the cubic
lattice through identical coils each with inductance L. All points
in the cubic network (like O) are connected to ground through
identical capacitors each with capacitance C. Although Kron
and his collaborators have used the periodic network shown in
Fig. 6.15 to treat the propagation of electromagnetic waves in
terms of the electric and magnetic fields, we will outline the
method in terms of the magnetic vector potential **A**. As no
source of current is attached to the point O, the sum of all the
currents flowing away from that point must vanish. Hence, we
may write the expression for the ac current flowing away from
point O as

$$- \frac{1}{i\omega L} \sum_{i=1}^{6} V_i + \left(\frac{6}{i\omega L} + i\omega C \right) V_O = 0, \qquad (605.8)$$

in which V_i is the amplitude of ac voltage that would be indicated by an ac voltmeter connected between ground and points $i = 0, 1, 2, 3, 4, 5,$ and 6. However, we use the Coulomb gauge, which requires that the scalar potential vanish so that V_i does not represent the scalar potential, but rather is related to the electric field E and the magnetic vector potential as indicated by the following relations:

$$\lim_{a \to 0} (V_1 - V_O)/a = (\dot{A}_1)_O = -(E_1)_O, \qquad (605.9)$$

$$\lim_{a \to 0} (V_3 - V_O)/a = (\dot{A}_2)_O = -(E_2)_O, \qquad (605.10)$$

$$\lim_{a \to 0} (V_5 - V_O)/a = (\dot{A}_3)_O = -(E_3)_O. \qquad (605.11)$$

The coordinates of the point O and its six nearest neighbors are listed in Table 6.1, from which it may be seen that the periodic network has a lattice constant a. Multiplying (605.8) through by $-i\omega L$, dividing through by a^2, and letting $L = \mu a$, and $C = \varepsilon a$, with μ and ε denoting the permeability and permittivity respectively of the transparent, homogeneous, isotropic medium represented by the network, we have the relation

$$\left[\sum_{i=1}^{6} (V_i - 6V_O)/a^2 \right] + \omega^2 \mu \varepsilon V_O = 0. \qquad (605.12)$$

The limit of (605.12) with $a \to 0$ gives the steady state differential wave equation

$$\nabla^2 V + \omega^2 \mu \varepsilon V = 0. \qquad (605.13)$$

The amplitude of the current flowing away from point O in the x direction is given by the relation

$$\dot{q}_{10} = (V_1 - V_O)/i\omega L. \qquad (605.14)$$

Hence, we may write

$$\frac{L\dot{q}_{10}}{a} = \frac{V_1 - V_O}{i\omega a} = \frac{\dot{A}_1}{i\omega} = A_1. \qquad (605.15)$$

We have similar relations for the other two axes

$$\frac{L\dot{q}_{30}}{a} = A_2 \qquad\qquad (605.16)$$

and

$$\frac{L\dot{q}_{50}}{a} = A_3. \qquad\qquad (605.17)$$

It follows automatically from (605.9)–(605.11) that

$$\mathbf{E} + \dot{\mathbf{A}} = 0, \qquad\qquad (605.18)$$

a well known relation which applies under the Coulomb gauge. It also follows from (605.9)–(605.11), together with the gradient of (605.13), that we may write as the steady state wave equation for the electric field

$$\nabla^2 \mathbf{E} + \omega^2 \mu \varepsilon \, \mathbf{E} = 0. \qquad\qquad (605.19)$$

Hence, in the limiting case with $a \to 0$, the periodic network under discussion supports the propagation of classical electromagnetic waves in the same manner as a homogeneous, isotropic, transparent medium, and such networks may be used as analog computers to solve the wave equation by methods which are essentially the same as those described in Section 6.0.1 in connection with analog computers designed to solve Poisson's equation.

6.1. Conjugate Quantities

A few highlights of classical mechanics are added here to form the basis for a discussion of several important relations in modern physics. Let us introduce Hamilton's canonical equations

$$\dot{y}_i = \partial \mathcal{H} / \partial p_i, \qquad \dot{p}_i = -\partial \mathcal{H} / \partial y_i, \qquad (610.1)$$

in which $\mathcal{H}$ is the Hamiltonian function defined by (310.10), and p_i is the momentum associated with the coordinate y_i as defined by (400.11). Two variables y_i and p_i which satisfy (610.1), are said to be canonically conjugate, and in the general sense, a coordinate and its corresponding momentum are canonically conjugate quantities. Some common coordinates and their corresponding momenta were listed in Table 4.1. It is well known that time becomes a component of a vector in the theory of relativity. If we return to Section 3.1, and extend the same argument by taking the time t as another coordinate on the same basis as each of the y_i, with each y_i and t as functions of some parameter t' which now plays the role heretofore assigned to the time, we may form the action integral, apply Hamilton's principle, and obtain a set of equations in which the time enters as one of the independent coordinates. By carrying out these steps one finds that the momentum corresponding to the time is the total energy E.

The most common conjugate quantities are listed in Table 6.2.

Some generalizations about the relationships between these conjugate quantities will be made in the remaining two sections.

TABLE 6.2

CONJUGATE QUANTITIES

Coordinate		Momentum	
Displacement	x	Momentum	p
Rotation	θ	Angular momentum	f
Charge	q	Magnetic flux	g
Time	t	Energy	E

6.1.1. Quantized Coordinates and Momenta

A quantized elastic wave or lattice vibration is called a *phonon*, and the momentum associated with a phonon is given by the product $\hbar k$, with h denoting Planck's constant and the line drawn through it indicating that it has been divided by 2π. Considering the lattice, treated in Section 6.0.2, it follows from the Born-Kármán conditions, that the momentum of a phonon is quantized and related to its fundamental period in the coordinate according to the following summary.

Coordinate period	Quantized momentum
Na (N is even)	$p = l\,(h/Na)$ (611.1) $l = 0, \pm 1, \pm 2, ..., \pm N/2$

Now consider the quantized magnetic flux bundles trapped in superconductors. It was discovered independently by Deaver and Fairbank (1961) and by Doll and Nabäuer (1961), that the magnetic flux in a superconductor is quantized, and that it represents a quantized momentum related to a coordinate period as indicated by the following relations.

Coordinate period	Quantized momentum
$2q_0$	$g = l\,(h/2q_0)$ (611.2) $l = 0, 1, 2, ...$

with q_0 the electronic charge.

It is implicit in the formulation of the equation of motion of the steady state behavior of an electron in an atom that its motion is periodic in an angular coordinate about an axis of rotation. According to quantum mechanics, the component of angular momentum f_i about the y_i axis is quantized in the manner indicated by the following relations.

Coordinate period	Quantized momentum
2π	$f_i = \frac{1}{2} l \, (h/2\pi)$ $l = \pm 1, \pm 2, \pm 3, \ldots$ (611.3)

It is also implicit in the equation of motion of the steady state behavior of an electron in an atom that the solution is periodic in time. If we take τ as the period assumed in the steady state solution, then we are justified in saying that time is quantized, as the solution is the same after each period τ in the same way that it is the same after each rotation by 2π. If we restrict ourselves to simple atomic and molecular systems, which may be approximated by quantum oscillators (an atom in the wall of a cavity as considered with black radiation, or the simple model of a molecule used to illustrate vibrational spectra) the energy may be written $(l+\frac{1}{2})(h/\tau)$. Hence, the momentum associated with the time is quantized and related to the period in the coordinate as given in the following summary.

Coordinate period	Quantized momentum
τ	$E = (l + \frac{1}{2})(h/\tau)$ $l = 0, 1, 2, \ldots$ (611.4)

Generalizing from the above, it may be seen that the momentum is quantized, and takes on a series of discrete values determined by integers. The momentum in each of the four examples given is a multiple of a fundamental momentum. In each case the fundamental momentum is given by Planck's constant divided by a periodic length in the coordinate, e.g., the periodic length in the superconductor consists of a pair of electrons with opposite spin; the multiple is an integer in two cases (611.1) and (611.2), $\frac{1}{2}$ times an integer in a third case (611.3) and $\frac{1}{2}$ plus an integer in the fourth case (611.4).

In addition to the harmonic relations between conjugate quantities, there are inherent limitations on the accuracy with which they may be determined. These limitations are discussed in the following section.

6.1.2. Uncertainty Relations[†]

A physical event happening in time t and having associated with it an amplitude $V(t)$ may be represented as shown in Fig. 6.16(a). This same event may be specified equally well in terms of its Fourier transform $v(\omega)$ which is plotted against frequency ω in Figure 6.16(b). Thus, we may say that the event may be

Fig. 6.16a. The physical property $V(t)$ associated with an event plotted against time t.

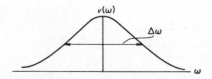

Fig. 6.16b.   The Fourier transform $v(\omega)$ of the same physical property plotted against the frequency ω.

[†] Figures 6.16 and 6.17 and some of the arguments presented in this section have already appeared elsewhere (Gossick, 1963).

specified either in the time domain or in the frequency domain.
If an event takes place in a very short time, requiring the width
Δt in Fig. 6.16(a) to be small, then it follows in general from
(210.48) that the corresponding width $\Delta\omega$ in Fig. 6.16(b) must
be very broad. This means that a very broad frequency spectrum
is required to define an event which is narrowly restricted in time.
Conversely, if the frequency spectrum of a phenomenon is confined within narrow limits, making $\Delta\omega$ small in Fig. 6.16(b), the
time width Δt in Fig. 6.16(a) must expand to a large value. This
inherent relation between time and frequency has the following
consequence. The width of the frequency spectrum of a physical
phenomenon cannot be determined in less than a given interval
of time. In fact, a perfectly precise measurement of frequency is
impossible, because this would require $\Delta\omega$ to vanish in Fig.
6.16(b), which would at the same time require Δt to expand to
plus and minus infinity in Fig. 6.16(a). This inherent limitation
on the determination of either frequency or time goes under the
name of the *uncertainty principle*. The following example illustrates the uncertainty principle through a familiar case. A piano
tuner, using a tuning fork to provide an absolute frequency
reference ω_0 attempts to tune one of the strings on a piano in
unison with this reference. As the tuner varies the tension of the
string so as to bring its pitch ω in unison with that of the fork,
he counts the beats, i.e., the pulses of sound which have the
frequency of the difference between the frequency of the string
and that of the fork. He counts in a given time interval Δt, the
number of beats equal to the product of the difference of the two
frequencies and the time interval.

$$(\omega - \omega_0)\,\Delta t = \text{number of beats times } 2\pi. \qquad (612.1)$$

In order to determine the frequency difference with any accuracy,
the tuner must be able to hear at least one beat. Therefore, the
product must equal or exceed unity, i.e., the following relation
must be satisfied.

$$(\omega - \omega_0)\,\Delta t \geqslant 1 \cdot 2\pi. \qquad (612.2)$$

In quantized systems, the frequency is linearly related to the energy (611.4), with Planck's constant being the constant of proportionality, and we may write $E = \hbar\omega$. Therefore, a relationship between the time and frequency is tantamount to a relation between the coordinate time and its conjugate momentum, the energy. Multiplying both sides of (612.2) by $\hbar$ gives the uncertainty relation,

$$\Delta E \, \Delta t \geqslant h. \tag{612.3}$$

Consider an event with the physical property $V(x_1, x_2)$ which depends on the two space coordinates x_1 and x_2 as shown in Fig. 6.17(a). The quantities which correspond to the x_1 and x_2

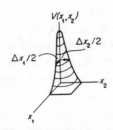

Fig. 6.17a.   The physical property $V(x_1, x_2)$ associated with an event plotted against space coordinates x_1 and x_2.

coordinates as the frequency corresponded to the time in the previous example are the wave vectors k_1 and k_2 respectively. The event may be specified completely in terms of the Fourier transform $v(k_1, k_2)$ indicated in Fig. 6.17b. Once more, the general mathematical relation (210.48) requires large spectral widths Δk_1 and Δk_2 in the Fourier transform [Fig. 6.17b] to specify an event sharply localized in space as indicated by narrow widths Δx_1 and Δx_2. The same principle applies to the determination of a region in x_1, x_2, x_3 space as opposed to the corresponding region in the k_1, k_2, k_3 domain. The arguments that

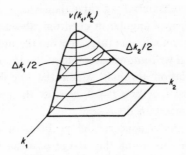

Fig. 6.17b. The Fourier transform $v(k_1, k_2)$ of the same physical property plotted against wave vectors k_1 and k_2.

were used in connection with relations (612.1)–(612.3) apply to any conjugate pair as well as another, and we may write

$$\Delta k_1 \, \Delta x_1 \geqslant 2\pi. \tag{612.4}$$

And, as the component of linear momentum p_1 equals $\hbar k_1$, we have

$$\Delta p_1 \, \Delta x_1 \geqslant h. \tag{612.5}$$

Let us now apply (612.4) to the example of lattice vibrations treated in Section 6.0.2 in order to determine $(\Delta x)_{\min}$ from the relation $(\Delta k)_{\max} (\Delta x)_{\min} \geqslant 2\pi$. Figure 6.4 shows the frequency plotted against the wave vector with k within the range $-\pi/a \leqslant k \leqslant +\pi/a$. Confining k within this range, it follows that $(\Delta k)_{\max} = 2\pi/a$. Therefore $(\Delta x)_{\min} \geqslant a$. Thus, it seems on the basis of this argument that if we restrict k to the range $-\pi/a \leqslant k \leqslant +\pi/a$ (which accounts for all possible frequencies), we are not justified in using the differential wave equation, i.e., Hill's equation (602.18) and (602.19), and have no alternative but to use the difference equation (602.5). If we want to use Hill's equation, we must employ k values outside the interval $-\pi/a \leqslant k \leqslant +\pi/a$, but this also leads to a dilemma. Just try to draw a picture of either a longitudinal or transverse wave in a lattice with $|k|$ substantially greater than π/a.

The component of angular momentum, about a given axis, of an electron is a definite quantity, obeying the quantum relation (611.3). This is a well-known example of the limiting case of the uncertainty relation through which the angular momentum may be specified exactly $\Delta f_i = 0$, because the angle of rotation is completely uncertain $\Delta \theta_i = \infty$.

The final remarks concern the problem of simultaneously determining the flux g and the charge q, using the simple LC circuit, as treated by Gossick (1966). We consider part of the capacitance to be that of the input of a high impedance detector which indicates the potential difference across the capacitor as a function of the time. Assuming that the inductance L and the capacitance C are known, the flux g and the charge q may be obtained from the determination of the potential difference across the inductance and capacitance connected in parallel as a function of the time from the relations

$$g = L(C \, \Delta V / \Delta t) \tag{612.6}$$

and

$$q = CV. \tag{612.7}$$

For a given increment of charge Δq the energy stored in the electric field within the capacitor is increased by the amount

$$\Delta E = (q/C) \, \Delta q, \tag{612.8}$$

and, at the same time, the energy stored in the magnetic field of the coil has been reduced in the same amount. As the coil and capacitor are connected in parallel, the voltage across the capacitor q/C must equal the potential difference across the coil as given by Faraday's law, $\Delta g / \Delta t$ with Δt small. This, we may write (612.8) in the form

$$\Delta E = (\Delta g / \Delta t) \, \Delta q. \tag{612.9}$$

Therefore, by multiplying both sides of (612.9) by Δt we find that the product $\Delta g\, \Delta q$ equals $\Delta E\, \Delta t$. As $\Delta E\, \Delta t$ is, in general, subject to the uncertainty relation, it follows that that statement may also be written in the form

$$\Delta g\, \Delta q \geqslant h, \tag{612.10}$$

which sets a limit on the accuracy of a simultaneous determination of magnetic flux and associated electric charge based on observations of voltage against time and relations (612.6) and (612.7).

When must one use quantum arguments in order to specify the deviations in magnetic flux and electric charge? Regarding the LC circuit classically, the thermal fluctuations are $\Delta g \sim (L\kappa T)^{\frac{1}{2}}$ and $\Delta q \sim (C\kappa T)^{\frac{1}{2}}$. Thus, if $\kappa T\,(LC)^{\frac{1}{2}} \gg h$, one may ignore quantum deviations. However, when microwaves are used in cryogenics, quantum deviations may dominate the noise, a case in point would be a simple cavity with resonant frequency of 3000 MHz at temperatures of 1°K and below.

Exercises

(6.1) (a) Consider a low pass electric filter composed of cascade connected T-sections (Fig. 6.6). Show that the characteristic impedance is given by the expression

$$Z_0 = \left[\frac{L}{C}\left(1 - \frac{\omega^2}{\omega_{max}^2} \right) \right]^{\frac{1}{2}}$$

with $\omega_{max} = 2/(LC)^{\frac{1}{2}}$.

(b) Consider a low pass electric filter composed of cascade connected Π-sections (Fig. 6.7). Show that the characteristic admittance is given by the expression

$$Y_0 = \left[\frac{C}{L}\left(1 - \frac{\omega^2}{\omega_{max}^2} \right) \right]^{\frac{1}{2}}$$

with ω_{max} the same as in (a).

(6.2) (a) Consider a high pass electric filter with a T-section unit cell as shown below.

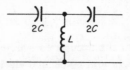

Show that the characteristic impedance is given by the following expression,

$$Z_0 = \left[\frac{L}{C} \left(1 - \frac{\omega_{min}^2}{\omega^2} \right) \right]^{\frac{1}{2}}$$

with $\omega_{min} = 1/2(LC)^{\frac{1}{2}}$.

(b) Consider a high pass electric filter with a Π-section unit cell as shown below.

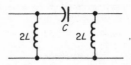

Show that the characteristic admittance is given by the following expression,

$$Y_0 = \left[\frac{C}{L} \left(1 - \frac{\omega_{min}^2}{\omega^2} \right) \right]^{\frac{1}{2}}$$

with ω_{min} the same as in (a).

(6.3) Consider a uniform transmission line with L, C, R, and G representing series inductance shunt capacitance, series resistance, and shunt conductance respectively, per unit length. Take the special case in which the following relation holds, $R/L = G/C$, which is the special condition prescribed by Heaviside for a *distortionless line*. Show that the complex wave vector and characteristic impedance are given by the following expressions

$$k^* = \omega(LC)^{\frac{1}{2}} - i\,G(L/C)^{\frac{1}{2}}, \quad \text{and} \quad Z_0 = (L/C)^{\frac{1}{2}}.$$

Explain why these characteristics guarantee that the spectral components of a signal will arrive at the end of a matched line in the same sequence as they entered and with the same relative amplitudes.

(6.4) Consider the junction at which two transmission lines are connected. Subscripts 1 and 2 are used to differentiate the properties associated with the two lines. An electrical signal propagating in the line designated by subscript 1 is incident on the junction and the components of the signal reflected by the junction are designated by primes. It is assumed that the other end of the line 2 is terminated in its characteristic impedance. The problem here is to determine the current and voltage reflection coefficients $\dot{q}_1'/\dot{q}_1$ and V_1'/V_1 respectively, and the current and voltage transmission coefficients $\dot{q}_2/\dot{q}_1$ and V_2/V_1 respectively. Given the continuity conditions at the junction: $\dot{q}_1 + \dot{q}_1' = \dot{q}_2$ and $V_1 + V_1' = V_2$, and the Ohm's law relations

$$V_1 = Z_1\dot{q}_1, \quad V_1' = -Z_1\dot{q}_1', \quad V_2 = Z_2\dot{q}_2,$$

show that

$$\frac{\dot{q}_1'}{\dot{q}_1} = \frac{Z_1 - Z_2}{Z_1 + Z_2} = -\frac{V_1'}{V_1},$$

$$\frac{\dot{q}_2}{\dot{q}_1} = \frac{2Z_1}{Z_1 + Z_2}, \quad \text{and} \quad \frac{V_2}{V_1} = \frac{2Z_2}{Z_1 + Z_2},$$

with Z_1 and Z_2 designating the characteristic impedances of lines 1 and 2.

If line 2 did not terminate in its characteristic impedance then we would account for the reflections from its termination by substituting an expression of the kind (604.15) for Z_2 in the above expressions for the reflection and transmission coefficients.

The reflection coefficient given here may be used by analogy to treat thermal scattering of an electron by a crystal lattice vibration in the one-dimensional approximation (Shockley, 1950). In this example the reflection coefficient for a scattering object of infinite length was used, i.e., the multiple reflections within the scattering object were ignored.

(6.5) Consider two uniform transmission lines with characteristic impedances Z_1 and Z_2 respectively, which are connected by a transition section of exactly a quarter wavelength of a third transmission line with characteristic impedance Z_0. Show that if the characteristic impedance Z_0 of the quarter wavelength line equals the geometric mean $(Z_1 Z_2)^{\frac{1}{2}}$ of the two lines between which it is connected, then the junction is nonreflecting for electrical signals incident on it from either direction. Such a transition section is called a *quarter wave matching transformer*, and in practice it operates satisfactorily for a narrow band of frequencies centered at the quarter wave frequency. The same principle is involved in nonreflecting lens coatings which function as optical quarter wave matching transformers.

(6.6) Consider the lossless transmission line shown in Fig. 6.9 which is matched at the input and short circuited at the output. Show that, if the output termination is changed to an open circuit, the response $V_2(t)$ to an input pulse $V_1(t)$ is given by the expression

$$V_2(t) = \tfrac{1}{2} \left[V_1(t) H(t) + V_1 \left(t - 2(LC)^{\frac{1}{2}} l \right) H \left(t - 2(LC)^{\frac{1}{2}} l \right) \right].$$

(6.7) Consider a hypothetical capacitor whose plates are formed by two identical strips of silver foil with thickness 30 μ, width 1 cm, and length 10 cm. The dielectric consists of a plastic film with dielectric properties resembling those of mica with a relative permittivity $\varepsilon/\varepsilon_0 = 7$. In order to provide a compact package for encapsulation, the dielectric film and conducting foils are folded into the geometric arrangement sketched below. Determine the behavior of this system in the frequency range between 500 and 600 MHz.

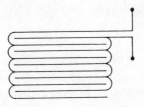

This problem demonstrates the necessity of the requirement that a circuit element be small compared with a wavelength. At high frequencies where the requirement is violated, the capacitor no longer behaves like one.

(6.8) Consider a lossless tapered transmission line with inductance per unit length and capacitance per unit length given by the following exponential functions of the position coordinate x:

$$L(x) = L_0 e^{ax}, \qquad (1)$$

$$C(x) = C_0 e^{-ax}. \qquad (2)$$

At first, consider the line to extend on the right to infinity. By an argument similar to that at the beginning of Section 6.0.4, show that the following relations for the tapered line correspond respectively to (604.4) and (604.8) for a uniform line.

$$\frac{dZ(x)}{dx} = y(x)[Z(x)]^2 - z(x), \qquad (3)$$

$$\frac{dV(x)}{dx} + \frac{z(x)V(x)}{Z(x)} = 0. \qquad (4)$$

Verify that $Z(x) = Z_e e^{ax}$ is a solution for (3) and (4) with

$$Z_e = \left[\frac{L_0}{C_0} - \frac{a^2}{4\omega^2 C_0{}^2}\right]^{\frac{1}{2}} + \frac{a}{2i\omega C_0}, \tag{5}$$

$$I(x,t) = I(0) \ \exp[i(\omega t - kx) - ax/2], \tag{6}$$

$$V(x,t) = Z_e I(0) \ \exp[i(\omega t - kx) + ax/2], \tag{7}$$

and

$$k = [\omega^2 L_0 C_0 - a^2/4]^{\frac{1}{2}}. \tag{8}$$

Thus, a finite line extending from $x = 0$ to $x = l$, terminates in an impedance Z_e at $x = 0$, and $Z_e e^{al}$ at $x = l$ is matched, and the above expressions for current and voltage apply in the range $0 \leqslant x \leqslant l$. Note that this tapered line is a high pass filter, and show that the cutoff frequency may be written as

$$\omega_{\min} = \left(\ln\left[V(l)/V(0)\right]\right)/l(L_0 C_0)^{\frac{1}{2}}, \tag{9}$$

with the input to output voltage ratio given by the fraction $V(l)/V(0)$. Thus, for a given length of line, the greater the ratio $V(l)/V(0)$ the higher the minimum frequency $\omega_{\min}$; and for a given ratio $V(l)/V(0)$, the shorter the line the higher is $\omega_{\min}$.

(6.9) Consider the filter circuit approximation of the tapered line treated in the previous exercise as illustrated by the accompanying circuit diagram.

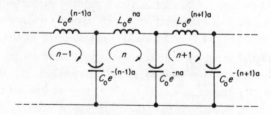

Designating the mesh current in the nth mesh I_n, we may express the steady state form for the voltage drops summed around the nth mesh as

$$-\frac{I_{n-1}e^{(n-1)a}}{i\omega C_0} + \left(i\omega L_0 e^{na} + \frac{e^{(n-1)a} - e^{na}}{i\omega C_0}\right)I_n - \frac{I_{n+1}e^{na}}{i\omega C_0} = 0. \quad (1)$$

As in the previous exercise, we assume first that the filter has an infinite number of sections so as to preclude reflections. On the basis of the solution for the continuous exponential line in the previous exercise, test the following expression for a current wave propagating in the direction of increasing n as a trial solution.

$$I_m(t) = I_0 \exp\left[i\left(\omega t - km\right) - ma/2\right]. \quad (2)$$

Show that (2) is a solution to (1) by substituting (2) into (1) letting m equal $n-1$, n, and $n+1$. Show that the filter circuit approximation of an exponential line is a band pass filter with

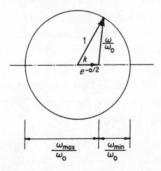

the pass band given by the accompanying construction, which gives the lower and upper cutoff frequencies as $\omega_{min} = \omega_0(1 - e^{-a/2})$ and $\omega_{max} = \omega_0(1 + e^{-a/2})$ respectively with $\omega_0 = (L_0 C_0)^{-\frac{1}{2}}$. Now assume that the filter has N sections and is matched at both ends. Show that the output to input voltage ratio is related to the bandwidth as indicated by the expression

$$\frac{V(N)}{V(0)} = e^{Na/2} = \left(\frac{\omega_{max} + \omega_{min}}{\omega_{max} - \omega_{min}}\right)^N.$$

Show that with a broad band width $\omega_{min} \ll \omega_{max}$, the output to input voltage ratio is given approximately by the relation

$$V(N)/V(0) = 1 + 2N(\omega_{min}/\omega_{max}).$$

Thus, in order to obtain simultaneously a broad bandwidth and a large output to input voltage ratio, a very large number of filter sections is required.

References

ADLER, R. B., CHU, L. J., and FANO, R. M. (1960). "Electromagnetic Energy Transmission and Radiation," Wiley, New York.

BODE, H. W. (1940), *Bell Syst. Tech. J.* **19**, 421 (1940).

BODE, H. W. (1945). "Network Analysis and Feedback Amplifier Design," Van Nostrand, New York.

BOOKER, H. G. (1941). *J. Inst. Elec. Engrs. (London)* **94**, 171.

BRILLOUIN, L. (1946). "Wave Propagation in Periodic Structures," Mc-Graw-Hill; 2nd. ed. Dover, New York (1963).

CASIMIR, H. B. G. (1963), *Proc. IEEE* **51**, 1570.

CAUCHY, A. L. (1815). "Theorie de la Propagation des Ondes (Prix d'analyse mathématique)," Concours de 1815 et de 1816, pp. 140, 141, 142, 281, and 282.

DEAVER, B., and FAIRBANK, W. (1961). *Phys. Rev. Letters* **7**, 43.

DOLL, R., and NÄBAUER, M. (1961). *Phys. Rev. Letters* **7**, 51.

DOW, W. G. (1952). "Fundamentals of Engineering Electronics," 2nd ed., Wiley, New York.

FIRESTONE, F. A. (1957). The Mobility and Classical Impedance Analogies, *in* "American Institute of Physics Handbook," McGraw-Hill, New York.

GARDNER, M. F., and BARNES, J. L. (1942). "Transients in Linear Systems," Wiley, New York.

GOSSICK, B. R. (1963). In "Electromagnetic Scattering" (M. Kerker, ed.), pp. 417–438. Pergamon Press, Oxford.

GOSSICK, B. R. (1963). *IEEE Trans. Education* **E-6**, 13–18.

GOSSICK, B. R. (1966). *Electron. Letters* **2**, 133.

GOSSICK, B. R. (1967). *IEEE Trans. Education E-10*, March.

HEAVISIDE, O. (1889). *Phil. Mag.* **27**, 324.

JAMES, H. M., and WEISS, P. R. (1947). "Theory of Servomechanisms" (JAMES, NICHOLS, and PHILLIPS, eds.), Chap. 2. McGraw-Hill, New York; reprinted by Dover, New York (1965).

KRON, G. (1935). Gen. Elec. Rev. **38**, 181.

KRON, G. (1959). "Tensors for Circuits," 2nd. ed. Dover, New York.

KRON, G. (1943). *Phys. Rev.* **64**, 126.

KRON, G. (1944). *Proc. IRE* **32**, 289.

LORENTZ, H. A. (1892). *Archives Néerlandaises* **25**, 363.

MASON, W. P., HEWITT, W. H., and WICK, R. F. (1953). *J. Appl. Phys.* **24**, 166–175.

MAXWELL, J. C. (1877). "Matter and Motion." Reprinted by Dover, New York.

MCALLISTER, J. F., Jr. (1944). *Gen. Elec. Rev.* **47**, 9.

NYQUIST, H. (1932). *Bell System Tech. J.* **11**, 126–147.

OLSON, H. F. (1943). "Dynamical Analogies." Van Nostrand, New York.

OLSON, H. F. (1947). "Elements of Acoustical Engineering." Van Nostrand, New York.

POISSON, S. D. (1816). Mémoire sur la Théorie des Ondes, *Mémoires de l'Academie des Sciences* 1, 71.

ROUTH, E. J. (1892). Adams Prize Essay for 1877, "Dynamics of a System of Rigid Bodies," 5th ed. Macmillan, London.

RYDER, R. M., and KIRCHER, R. J. (1949). *Bell System Tech. J.* 28, 367–401.

SCHELKUNOFF, S. A. (1938). *Bell System Tech. J.* 17, 17.

SHOCKLEY, W. (1949). Bell Syst. Tech. J. 28, 435.

SHOCKLEY, W. (1950). "Electrons and Holes in Semiconductors," pp. 267–268, Van Nostrand, New York.

SMITH, P. H. (1939). *Electronics* 12, 29.

SPANGENBERG, K. R. (1948). "Vacuum Tubes." McGraw-Hill, New York.

STRUTT, J. W. (Lord Rayleigh) (1873). *Proc. Math. Soc., June 1873*.

STRUTT, J. W. (Lord Rayleigh) (1887). "The Theory of Sound," Vol. 1; reprinted by Dover, New York (1945).

WEISS, H. (1956). *Z. Naturforsch.* 11a, 684–688.

WEISS, H. (1964). *Solid-State Electron.* 4, 279.

WHINNERY, J. R., and RAMO, S. (1944). *Proc. IRE* 32, 284.

WHINNERY, J. R., CONCORDIA, C., RIDGWAY, W., and KRON, G. (1944). *Proc. IRE* 32, 360.

WICK, R. F. (1954). *J. Appl. Phys.* 25, 741–756.

Subject Index